Problems

Solve each problem.

1. Odometer readings, such as shown above, tell how many miles a car has been driven. What is the total number of miles cars A and B have been driven?

Car A has been driven _____ miles.

Car B has been driven _____ miles.

Both cars have been driven _____ miles.

2. How many more miles has car A been driven than car C?

Car A has been driven _____ miles.

Car C has been driven _____ miles.

Car A has been driven _____ more miles.

3. What is the total number of miles car A, car B, and car C have been driven?

They have been driven _____ miles.

1.

2.

3.

PRE-TEST—Addition and Subtraction

Add or subtract.

	a	*b*	*c*	*d*	*e*	*f*
1.	35 +3	7 +43	43 +25	67 +28	73 +52	59 +63
2.	46 −5	57 −9	28 −13	148 −63	175 −86	214 −35
3.	421 +348	325 +436	783 +192	752 +638	428 +173	976 +544
4.	738 −125	872 −439	986 −394	1465 −938	1831 −256	3814 −915

Add or subtract.

	a	*b*	*c*	*d*	*e*
5.	4218 +3570	5831 +4179	6281 +3982	7543 +9647	2796 +8215
6.	7832 −4701	4216 −2437	52614 −8316	38126 −9433	42713 −5816
7.	53246 +32512	42186 +17287	38743 +45382	20917 +34216	52843 +28379
8.	82165 −31042	32186 −9178	42514 −3495	88672 −32967	98135 −28459
9.	42 26 +38	523 416 +758	4281 3826 +1435	42163 5286 +25488	32815 12916 +38442

Addition

Add the ones.
Rename 19 as 10 + 9.

Add the tens.

```
   5 7              7          →  ¹5 7          ¹5 7
     4              4               4              4
 + 6 8           + 8           + 6 8          + 6 8
 ───────         ─────         ───────        ───────
                 1 9 or 10 + 9      9          1 2 9
```

Add.

	a	b	c	d	e	f
1.	3 4 + 5	6 +2 1	4 8 + 5	9 +3 6	5 6 + 3	9 +7 8
2.	3 5 +2 4	4 6 +3 2	3 7 +4 1	2 0 +5 8	3 1 +3 8	6 5 +1 3
3.	5 7 +2 4	3 6 +2 7	5 8 +1 9	5 2 +9 4	3 2 +7 1	5 5 +9 3
4.	3 5 +8 9	7 2 +7 9	8 6 +4 5	4 8 +6 3	3 7 +6 5	5 4 +9 8
5.	3 5 3 +2 1	2 7 1 8 +3 5	4 2 3 +7 0	5 2 1 6 +5 9	3 5 2 7 + 6	5 8 3 7 +2 9
6.	3 6 8 4 2 7 +3 9	4 2 5 9 2 6 + 7	2 1 8 5 4 +2 6	8 3 7 5 8 +7 5	3 1 8 0 6 0 + 9	5 4 5 4 5 4 +5 4

Subtraction

Rename 72 as "6 tens and 12 ones." Subtract the ones.

Rename 1 hundred and 6 tens as "16 tens." Subtract the tens.

$$\begin{array}{r} 1\ 7\ 2 \\ -\ 9\ 6 \\ \hline \end{array}$$

$$\begin{array}{r} 1\ \overset{6}{7}\ \overset{12}{2} \\ -\ 9\ 6 \\ \hline 6 \end{array}$$

$$\begin{array}{r} \overset{16}{1}\ \overset{6}{\cancel{7}}\ \overset{12}{\cancel{2}} \\ -\ 9\ 6 \\ \hline 7\ 6 \end{array}$$

Subtract.

	a	b	c	d	e	f
1.	57 −3	98 −4	63 −3	75 −6	38 −9	46 −8
2.	68 −25	75 −32	98 −44	37 −12	46 −36	58 −27
3.	53 −28	84 −36	61 −27	37 −18	25 −18	42 −25
4.	154 −27	193 −37	295 −27	146 −39	253 −27	104 −45
5.	163 −93	253 −62	357 −71	176 −83	483 −93	519 −34
6.	184 −97	352 −69	463 −87	108 −29	520 −83	645 −96

Addition

Add the ones.	Add the tens.	Add the hundreds. Rename 16 hundreds as "1 thousand and 6 hundreds."	Add the thousands.
3 3 1² 6 6 2 8 +8 7 3 7 _____ 1	3 3 ²1 6 6 2 8 +8 7 3 7 _____ 8 1	¹3 3 ²1 6 6 2 8 +8 7 3 7 _____ 6 8 1	¹3 3 ²1 6 6 2 8 +8 7 3 7 _____ 1 2 6 8 1

Add.

	a	b	c	d	e
1.	423 +165	527 +319	382 +476	528 +739	524 +898
2.	3168 +3240	3782 +4561	8093 +1279	5837 +2896	6789 +4567
3.	54312 +24241	52168 +29210	83245 +13876	42104 +49863	54372 +36798
4.	423 104 +735	1423 3410 +6578	4216 3807 +4218	42116 38425 +10731	22430 38654 +12465
5.	52316 4284 +3721	342 1563 +78216	1423 7386 +214	42305 316 +4217	5203 48310 +244
6.	342 153 786 +403	2173 4168 5246 +3700	4215 3800 2407 +3142	12421 33568 45423 +13154	12421 13685 17256 +60381
7.	421 3863 425 +38160	1725 42311 3820 +421	7526 380 62776 +5381	4270 38197 244 +42311	738 52865 376 +25400

Problems

Solve each problem.

1. A trucker drove 528 kilometers on the first trip and 746 kilometers on the next. How many kilometers did the trucker drive altogether?

_____ kilometers were driven on the first trip.

_____ kilometers were driven on the next trip.

_____ kilometers were driven altogether.

2. Xemo Corporation filled 5,281 orders last week and 7,390 orders this week. How many orders were filled in these two weeks?

_____ orders were filled last week.

_____ orders were filled this week.

_____ orders were filled in the two weeks.

3. Xemo Corporation produced 42,165 xemos in January and 34,895 xemos in February. How many xemos were produced in both January and February?

_____ xemos were produced in January.

_____ xemos were produced in February.

_____ xemos were produced in both months.

4. In three weeks Mr. Jenkins carried the following number of passengers on his bus: 4,216; 3,845; and 7,281. What was the total number of passengers carried in the three weeks?

_____ passengers were carried.

5. The odometer readings on the last three cars that Mr. Williams sold were 22,163; 48,395; and 23,842. How many miles were recorded on these three cars?

_____ miles were recorded.

6. Last month three jets were flown the following number of miles: 42,816; 5,421; and 38,652. What was the total number of miles flown?

_____ miles were flown.

1.	
2.	
3.	
4.	
5.	
6.	

SPECTRUM MATHEMATICS,
Green Book–Second Edition

Perfect score: 12   My score: _____

Subtraction

	Subtract the ones.	Rename. Subtract the tens.	Subtract the hundreds.	Continue to rename and subtract as needed.

$$
\begin{array}{r} 4\ 2\ 0\ 1\ {}^{7}\!\!\!\diagup \\ -\ 3\ 8\ 4\ 6 \\ \hline 1 \end{array}
\qquad
\begin{array}{r} 4\ 2\ 0\ \overset{9}{1}\ 7 \\ -\ 3\ 8\ 4\ 6 \\ \hline 7\ 1 \end{array}
\qquad
\begin{array}{r} 4\ 2\ \overset{9}{0}\ 1\ 7 \\ -\ 3\ 8\ 4\ 6 \\ \hline 1\ 7\ 1 \end{array}
\qquad
\begin{array}{r} 4\ \overset{11}{2}\ \overset{9}{0}\ 1\ 7 \\ -\ 3\ 8\ 4\ 6 \\ \hline 3\ 8\ 1\ 7\ 1 \end{array}
$$

Subtract.

	a	b	c	d	e
1.	736 −324	546 −329	831 −480	516 −337	703 −299
2.	4216 −314	2468 −539	5468 −573	2345 −456	1306 −457
3.	5246 −2215	3872 −2438	4351 −2263	4020 −1706	7503 −2455
4.	53211 −4298	42683 −3167	54216 −5299	60831 −7081	29540 −5219
5.	42465 −21528	38429 −14953	76543 −37835	82106 −47297	30907 −18608
6.	67230 −41195	42007 −18246	86992 −20997	71549 −10856	90036 −89595

Problems

Solve each problem.

1. It takes 500 points to win a prize. Pat has 385 points now. How many more points does she need to win a prize?

_____ points are needed to win a prize.

Pat now has _____ points.

She needs _____ more points.

2. There are 1,516 pupils enrolled at Webb School. Of these, 842 are girls. How many are boys?

_____ pupils are enrolled.

_____ of the pupils are girls.

_____ of the pupils are boys.

3. Factory A employs 5,281 people and factory B employs 3,817 people. How many more people does factory A employ than factory B?

Factory A employs _____ more people.

4. Mr. Wells had 52,816 miles on his car when he traded it. The car he traded for has 4,357 miles on it. How many fewer miles does it have than the older car?

It has _____ fewer miles.

5. Last year 42,169 orders were shipped from a warehouse. So far this year 5,837 orders have been shipped. How many more orders must be shipped this year in order to match the total for last year?

_____ more orders must be shipped.

6. The odometer on Jim's car reads 52,116. The odometer on Pat's car reads 38,429. How many more miles are on Jim's car than are on Pat's car?

_____ more miles are on Jim's car.

1.

2.

3.

4.

5.

6.

Addition and Subtraction

Add or subtract.

	a	b	c	d	e	f
1.	32 +6	5 +48	23 +35	47 +26	89 +50	78 +57
2.	58 −3	72 −21	47 −38	159 −93	143 −85	202 −37
3.	523 +364	428 +537	683 +194	385 +276	483 +629	753 +869
4.	783 −502	926 −418	564 −283	1925 −137	2436 −648	1926 −928

Add or subtract.

	a	b	c	d	e
5.	5231 +3468	4661 +2179	3157 +6930	2087 +9237	4281 +6759
6.	8426 −3312	7531 −3452	8426 −2756	13041 −9158	25308 −8499
7.	63125 +10420	42163 +45387	28135 +47385	61702 +28715	37839 +57893
8.	72519 −30418	83162 −35087	52083 −41839	98035 −68746	63613 −55895
9.	23 34 +42	426 709 +358	4216 5384 +2196	22514 43868 +21706	82965 372 +1451

Problems

Answer each question.

1. In a contest, Mary earned 758 points. Helen earned 929 points. Bill earned 1,356 points. How many points did the two girls earn?

Are you to add or subtract? _____

How many points did the two girls earn? _____

1.

2. In problem **1**, how many more points did Bill earn than Helen?

Are you to add or subtract? _____
How many more points did
  Bill earn than Helen? _____

2.

3. In problem **1**, how many points did all three people earn?

Are you to add or subtract? _____

How many points did all three earn? _____

3.

4. This month 32,526 people visited the museum. Last month 28,831 people visited the museum. How many more people visited the museum this month than last month?

Are you to add or subtract? _____
How many more people visited the
  museum this month than last month? _____

4.

5. In problem 4, how many people visited the museum during the two months?

Are you to add or subtract? _____
How many people visited the
  museum during the two months? _____

5.

6. At the beginning of last year 52,116 cars were registered. There were 4,913 new cars registered the first six months and 3,085 the second six months. How many cars were registered at the end of the year?

Are you to add or subtract? _____

How many cars were registered
  at the end of the year? _____

6.

TEST—Addition and Subtraction

Add or subtract.

	a	b	c	d	e
1.	42 +9	75 +83	96 +58	147 +129	345 +286
2.	54 −6	39 −27	158 −79	384 −215	580 −483
3.	4216 −3817	15382 −8293	42165 −38479	52163 −44318	84362 −53977
4.	5421 +8892	5843 +6969	52816 +32558	4235 6815 +42916	38433 12758 +28906

Answer each question.

5. At the end of last year, suppose the odometer reading on your car was 33,384. You drove your car 29,458 kilometers last year. What was the reading at the beginning of last year?

Are you to add or subtract? _____
What was the reading at
   the beginning of last year? _____

5.

6. In problem **5**, suppose you expect to drive the car the same number of kilometers this year as you did last year. If you do, what will the reading be at the end of this year?

Are you to add or subtract? _____
What will the reading be
   at the end of this year? _____

6.

7. Suppose the distances you drove in the last three years were 42,516 kilometers, 38,342 kilometers, and 14,208 kilometers. How many kilometers did you drive in three years?

How many kilometers did
   you drive in three years? _____

7.

PRE-TEST—Multiplication and Division

Multiply.

	a	*b*	*c*	*d*	*e*
1.	33 ×3	48 ×4	304 ×2	432 ×8	1234 ×2
2.	6789 ×5	133 ×21	456 ×34	1231 ×22	5783 ×45
3.	123 ×321	576 ×435	1302 ×132	4563 ×478	5009 ×837

Divide.

4.   25)225   14)518   27)463   14)4550   95)3610

5.   53)7832   92)12420   58)45530   32)78216   73)52914

Multiplication

Multiply.

	a	b	c	d	e	f	g	h
1.	4 ×0	2 ×0	8 ×0	1 ×0	7 ×1	6 ×1	1 ×1	5 ×1
2.	8 ×2	2 ×2	4 ×2	7 ×2	6 ×2	5 ×2	3 ×2	9 ×2
3.	9 ×3	7 ×3	5 ×3	0 ×3	1 ×3	6 ×3	4 ×3	3 ×3
4.	4 ×4	3 ×4	5 ×4	8 ×4	7 ×4	0 ×4	9 ×4	1 ×4
5.	8 ×5	2 ×5	7 ×5	5 ×5	4 ×5	3 ×5	1 ×5	0 ×5
6.	8 ×6	2 ×6	9 ×6	7 ×6	6 ×6	5 ×6	1 ×6	3 ×6
7.	9 ×7	7 ×7	6 ×7	0 ×7	1 ×7	5 ×7	8 ×7	4 ×7
8.	0 ×8	5 ×8	8 ×8	9 ×8	4 ×8	3 ×8	6 ×8	7 ×8
9.	3 ×9	9 ×9	8 ×9	1 ×9	2 ×9	7 ×9	6 ×9	4 ×9

SPECTRUM MATHEMATICS,
Green Book–Second Edition

Perfect score: 72   My score: _____

Division

Divide.

	a	*b*	*c*	*d*	*e*	*f*	*g*	*h*
1.	1)2	1)3	1)5	1)4	1)6	1)9	1)8	1)1
2.	2)18	2)12	2)14	2)16	2)8	2)10	2)4	2)2
3.	3)0	3)15	3)9	3)12	3)24	3)18	3)3	3)21
4.	4)20	4)8	4)4	4)12	4)32	4)24	4)36	4)16
5.	5)30	5)45	5)0	5)10	5)25	5)15	5)40	5)5
6.	6)30	6)24	6)42	6)6	6)12	6)36	6)54	6)48
7.	7)0	7)21	7)14	7)56	7)49	7)63	7)35	7)28
8.	8)16	8)0	8)56	8)72	8)48	8)32	8)24	8)40
9.	9)45	9)27	9)36	9)63	9)9	9)81	9)0	9)54

SPECTRUM MATHEMATICS,
Green Book–Second Edition

Perfect score: 72   My score: _____

Multiplication

Multiply 7 ones by 5.

$$\begin{array}{r} 9\ 8\ \overset{3}{1}\ 7 \\ \times 5 \\ \hline 5 \end{array}\qquad \begin{array}{r} 7 \\ \times 5 \\ \hline 35 \end{array}$$

Multiply 1 ten by 5. Add the 3 tens.

$$\begin{array}{r} 9\ 8\ \overset{3}{1}\ 7 \\ \times 5 \\ \hline 8\ 5 \end{array}\qquad \begin{array}{r} 10 \\ \times 5 \\ \hline 50 \\ +30 \\ \hline 80 \end{array}$$

Multiply 8 hundreds by 5.

$$\begin{array}{r} \overset{4}{9}\ 8\ \overset{3}{1}\ 7 \\ \times 5 \\ \hline 0\ 8\ 5 \end{array}\qquad \begin{array}{r} 800 \\ \times 5 \\ \hline 4000 \end{array}$$

Multiply 9 thousands by 5. Add the 4 thousands.

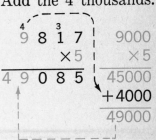

$$\begin{array}{r} \overset{4}{9}\ 8\ \overset{3}{1}\ 7 \\ \times 5 \\ \hline 4\ 9\ 0\ 8\ 5 \end{array}\qquad \begin{array}{r} 9000 \\ \times 5 \\ \hline 45000 \\ +4000 \\ \hline 49000 \end{array}$$

Multiply.

	a	*b*	*c*	*d*	*e*
1.	3 2 ×3	2 3 ×4	8 2 ×3	7 8 ×8	9 5 ×6
2.	4 2 1 ×2	1 2 3 ×4	2 4 1 ×3	5 0 1 ×5	1 5 9 ×6
3.	7 8 3 ×3	5 3 8 ×8	7 6 2 ×5	9 5 4 ×7	4 7 3 ×9
4.	1 0 3 3 ×2	3 2 1 6 ×3	3 1 7 2 ×3	5 0 1 4 ×2	3 2 5 7 ×3
5.	1 4 7 8 ×6	5 7 3 8 ×7	4 8 2 6 ×9	5 3 8 4 ×6	7 0 8 3 ×5

Problems

Solve each problem.

1. Mrs. Clarke has 24 pupils in her class. She gave each pupil 5 sheets of paper. How many sheets of paper did she use?

_____ pupils are in class.

_____ sheets of paper are given each pupil.

_____ sheets of paper are used.

2. Each bus can carry 77 passengers. How many passengers can be carried on 7 such buses?

Each bus can carry _____ passengers.

There are _____ buses in all.

A total of _____ passengers can be carried.

3. There are 365 days in a year, except leap year which has 366 days. How many days are there in 3 years if there is no leap year included?

There are _____ days in a year.

The number of days in _____ years is to be found.

There are _____ days in 3 years.

4. Seven hundred seventy-five meals were prepared each day for 5 days. How many meals were prepared in the 5 days?

_____ meals were prepared in the 5 days.

5. Michael earned 3,401 points. His sister earned twice as many. How many points did his sister earn?

His sister earned _____ points.

6. A machine is designed to produce 2,965 parts each day. How many parts should the machine produce in 7 days?

The machine should produce _____ parts in 7 days.

1.	
2.	
3.	4.
5.	6.

Multiplication

Multiply 4567 by 1.

```
  4567
×  321
──────
  4567
```

Multiply 4567 by 20.

```
  4567
×  321
──────
  4567
 91340
```

Multiply 4567 by 300.

```
  4567
×  321
──────
   4567
  91340
1370100
```

```
  4567
×  321
──────
   4567  ⎫
  91340  ⎬ Add.
1370100  ⎭
──────
1466007
```

Multiply.

	a	b	c	d	e
1.	57 ×21	48 ×32	75 ×63	135 ×48	276 ×42
2.	531 ×27	835 ×92	1864 ×27	3186 ×54	7083 ×92

Multiply.

	a	b	c	d
3.	413 ×214	564 ×532	217 ×416	908 ×592
4.	1564 ×795	3827 ×630	9216 ×205	5043 ×684

Problems

Solve each problem.

1. Each box weighs 28 kilograms. What is the weight of 35 such boxes?

Each box weighs _____ kilograms.

There are _____ boxes in all.

The total weight is _____ kilograms.

1.

2. There are 19 carpenters working for a construction firm. Each worked 47 hours last week. What is the total number of hours they worked last week?

Each carpenter worked _____ hours.

There are _____ carpenters in all.

_____ hours were worked.

2.

3. The production schedule estimates that 321 machines can be produced each week. At that rate, how many machines can be produced in 52 weeks?

There are _____ machines scheduled to be produced each week.

There are _____ weeks.

_____ machines can be produced in 52 weeks.

3.

4. The rail distance between Los Angeles and New York is 3,257 miles. How many miles would a train travel if it made 32 one-way trips between these two cities?

The train would travel _____ miles.

4.

5. There are 731 cases of zoopers in the warehouse. Each case contains 144 zoopers. How many zoopers are in the warehouse?

There are _____ zoopers in the warehouse.

5.

6. There are 1,440 minutes in one day. How many minutes are in 365 days?

There are _____ minutes in 365 days.

6.

SPECTRUM MATHEMATICS,
Green Book–Second Edition

Perfect score: 12   My score: _____

Division

Study how to divide 2074 by 6.

×	100	200	300	400
6	600	1200	1800	2400

2074 is between 1800 and 2400, so 2074 ÷ 6 is between 300 and 400. The hundreds digit is 3.

```
     3
6)2074
  1800    (300×6)
   274    Subtract.
```

×	10	20	30	40	50
6	60	120	180	240	300

274 is between 240 and 300, so 274 ÷ 6 is between 40 and 50. The tens digit is 4.

```
    34
6)2074
  1800
   274
   240    (40×6)
    34    Subtract.
```

×	1	2	3	4	5	6	7
6	6	12	18	24	30	36	42

34 is between 30 and 36, so 34 ÷ 6 is between 5 and 6. The ones digit is 5.

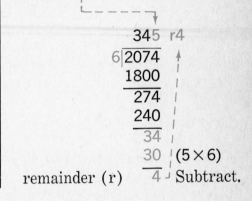

```
   345 r4
6)2074
  1800
   274
   240
    34
    30    (5×6)
     4    Subtract.
```

remainder (r)

Divide.

	a	b	c	d	e
1.	4)92	3)58	3)72	4)77	6)810
2.	3)225	6)590	6)8080	9)4739	6)4254

Problems

Solve each problem.

1. Mr. Wilson gave 5 sheets of paper to each pupil. He had 2 sheets left. He had 92 sheets to begin with. How many pupils received paper?

There were _____ sheets of paper in all.

Each pupil received _____ sheets of paper.

There were _____ pupils who received paper.

1.

2. Three people earned 774 points in a contest. Suppose each person earned the same number of points. How many points did each person earn?

Each person earned _____ points.

2.

3. As each new car comes off an assembly line, it receives 8 gallons of gasoline. How many new cars can receive gasoline from a tank containing 2,440 gallons?

_____ new cars can receive gasoline.

3.

4. Four baseballs are put in each box. How many boxes are needed to package 273 baseballs? How many baseballs would be left?

_____ boxes are needed.

_____ baseball would be left.

4.

5. A train travels 6,516 miles to make a round trip between New York and Los Angeles. How many miles would the train travel from Los Angeles to New York?

The train would travel _____ miles.

5.

6. Each carton holds 8 bottles. How many full cartons could be filled with 3,075 bottles? How many bottles would be left over?

_____ cartons could be filled.

_____ bottles would be left over.

6.

SPECTRUM MATHEMATICS,
Green Book—Second Edition

Perfect score: 10   My score: _____

Division

Study how to divide 28888 by 95.

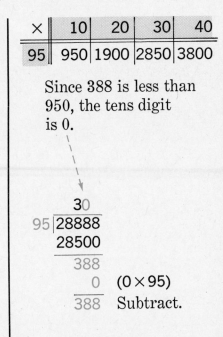

×	100	200	300	400
95	9500	19000	28500	38000

28888 is between 28500 and 38000, so 28888 ÷ 95 is between 300 and 400. The hundreds digit is 3.

```
        3
95 ) 28888
     28500   (300 × 95)
  ───────
       388   Subtract.
```

×	10	20	30	40
95	950	1900	2850	3800

Since 388 is less than 950, the tens digit is 0.

```
       30
95 ) 28888
     28500
  ───────
       388
         0   (0 × 95)
  ───────
       388   Subtract.
```

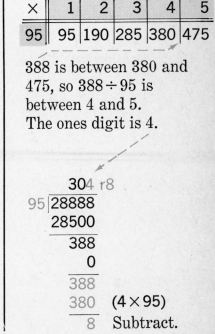

×	1	2	3	4	5
95	95	190	285	380	475

388 is between 380 and 475, so 388 ÷ 95 is between 4 and 5. The ones digit is 4.

```
      304 r8
95 ) 28888
     28500
  ───────
       388
         0
  ───────
       388
       380   (4 × 95)
  ───────
         8   Subtract.
```

Divide.

	a	b	c	d	e
1.	25) 810	33) 891	18) 819	27) 727	75) 6900
2.	54) 7695	28) 9698	98) 34937	75) 39400	42) 14742

Problems

Solve each problem.

1. There are 988 pupils enrolled at King School. There are 26 pupils in each class. How many classes are in King School?

_____ pupils are enrolled.

_____ pupils are in each class.

There are _____ classes in all.

2. Mr. Lodey has 987 parts to pack. He will pack 24 parts in each box. How many boxes will he need? How many parts will be left over?

He will need _____ boxes.

He will have _____ parts left over.

3. A bank considers 30 days to be a month. How many months would there be in 9,295 days? How many days would be left over?

There would be _____ months.

There would be _____ days left over.

4. During a two-week period, 75 employees worked a total of 5,625 hours. Each employee worked the same number of hours. How many hours did each employee work?

Each employee worked _____ hours.

5. There are 76 sections with a total of 17,100 seats in the new stadium. Each section has the same number of seats. How many seats are in each section?

There are _____ seats in each section.

6. Three dozen grapefruit are packed in a case. How many cases would be needed to pack 27,100 grapefruit? How many grapefruit would be left over?

_____ cases would be needed.

_____ grapefruit would be left over.

1.	2.
3.	4.
5.	6.

Perfect score: 11   My score: _____

Multiplication and Division

Multiply.

	a	b	c	d	e
1.	3 5 ×7	3 4 7 ×5	3 8 5 ×8	1 4 3 8 ×9	4 9 0 6 ×6
2.	3 7 ×8 5	4 8 ×5 4	3 5 7 ×9 2	2 8 9 ×3 8	4 3 5 6 ×2 7
3.	1 5 8 ×1 3 2	7 0 6 ×3 1 5	3 4 5 ×2 2 1	7 0 9 ×7 4 3	6 8 9 ×8 3 8

Divide.

4. 22) 3 8 6   35) 4 5 2   25) 9 5 0   12) 1 4 6 8   54) 8 4 7 8

5. 15) 3 0 9 2   75) 4 7 2 8   37) 1 5 7 2 5   53) 2 4 8 1 5   43) 4 5 6 8 3

SPECTRUM MATHEMATICS,
Green Book–Second Edition

Perfect score: 25   My score: _____

Problems

Answer each question.

1. It takes 75 hours to make one tractor. How many hours would it take to make 650 tractors?

Are you to multiply or divide? _____
How many hours would
   it take to make 650 tractors? _____

2. It takes 28 minutes to make one hubcap. How many hubcaps could be made in 196 minutes?

Are you to multiply or divide? _____
How many hubcaps could
   be made in 196 minutes? _____

3. There are 168 hours in one week. How many hours are in 260 weeks?

Are you to multiply or divide? _____
How many hours are
   in 260 weeks? _____

4. There were 5,790 tickets sold at the game. There are 75 tickets on a roll of tickets. How many complete rolls of tickets were sold? How many tickets from the next roll were sold?

Are you to multiply or divide? _____
How many complete
   rolls of tickets were sold? _____
How many tickets from the
   next roll were sold? _____

5. A satellite orbits the moon every 45 minutes. How many complete orbits could it make in 5,545 minutes? How many minutes would be left over?

Are you to multiply or divide? _____
How many complete
   orbits could be made? _____
How many minutes
   would be left over? _____

6. There are 10,080 minutes in a week. How many minutes are in 52 weeks?

Are you to multiply or divide? _____
How many minutes
   are in 52 weeks? _____

1.	2.
3.	4.
5.	6.

SPECTRUM MATHEMATICS,
Green Book–Second Edition

Perfect score: 14   My score: _____

TEST—Multiplication and Division

Multiply.

	a	b	c	d	e
1.	43 ×2	38 ×9	507 ×8	1351 ×6	7254 ×7
2.	35 ×23	48 ×76	155 ×33	2056 ×42	3718 ×37
3.	304 ×144	215 ×255	1403 ×304	5555 ×246	3182 ×354

Divide.

4. 34)136   12)420   53)781   37)4316   29)1702

5. 74)9990   46)1257   38)38640   14)53821   63)27342

PRE-TEST—Multiplication

Write each answer in simplest form.

	a	b	c	d
1.	$\frac{1}{2} \times \frac{3}{5}$	$\frac{4}{7} \times \frac{4}{5}$	$\frac{2}{3} \times \frac{5}{7}$	$\frac{2}{5} \times \frac{2}{5}$
2.	$\frac{3}{5} \times \frac{1}{6}$	$\frac{3}{8} \times \frac{5}{9}$	$\frac{6}{7} \times \frac{3}{8}$	$\frac{8}{9} \times \frac{3}{10}$
3.	$3 \times \frac{2}{5}$	$5 \times \frac{8}{9}$	$6 \times \frac{3}{4}$	$\frac{8}{9} \times 3$
4.	$4 \times 3\frac{1}{3}$	$2\frac{1}{2} \times 5$	$4 \times \frac{1}{6}$	$\frac{7}{8} \times 12$
5.	$2\frac{1}{3} \times 1\frac{1}{4}$	$1\frac{7}{8} \times 1\frac{2}{7}$	$4\frac{2}{3} \times 1\frac{3}{7}$	$3\frac{1}{3} \times 2\frac{2}{5}$

SPECTRUM MATHEMATICS,
Green Book–Second Edition

Perfect score: 20   My score: _____

Fractions

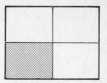

$\dfrac{2}{3}$ ← **numerator** ← – – –number of parts colored – – –→ numerator → ____

$\phantom{\dfrac{2}{3}}$ ← **denominator** ← – -number of parts of the same size-→ denominator →

$\dfrac{2}{3}$ of the triangle is colored.   ____ of the square is colored.

Write the fraction that tells how much of each figure is colored.

	a	*b*	*c*	*d*

1. ____   ____   ____   (pentagon) ____

2. ____   ____   ____   ____

Draw a line segment between each fraction and number word that name the same number.

     a   *b*

3. one half $\dfrac{4}{5}$ three eighths $\dfrac{7}{9}$

4. two thirds $\dfrac{3}{4}$ four sevenths $\dfrac{3}{8}$

5. three fourths $\dfrac{2}{3}$ three sevenths $\dfrac{3}{7}$

6. four fifths $\dfrac{1}{2}$ seven eighths $\dfrac{4}{7}$

7. five sixths $\dfrac{5}{6}$ seven ninths $\dfrac{7}{8}$

Write a fraction for each of the following.

     a   *b*

8. numerator 4, denominator 7 _____   three fifths _____

9. numerator 5, denominator 8 _____   two sevenths _____

10. denominator 10, numerator 9 _____   four ninths _____

SPECTRUM MATHEMATICS,
Green Book–Second Edition
          Perfect score: 24   My score: _____

Mixed Numerals

$\dfrac{13}{4}$ means $\begin{cases} 13 \div 4 \\ \text{or} \\ 4\overline{)13} \end{cases}$

$\begin{array}{r} 3\frac{1}{4} \\ 4\overline{)13} \\ 12 \\ \hline 1 \end{array} \to 1 \div 4 = \dfrac{1}{4}$

$3\frac{1}{4}$ is a short way to write $3 + \dfrac{1}{4}$.

$3\frac{1}{4}$ is a **mixed numeral.**

Complete the following.

	a	*b*	*c*	*d*
1.	$3\frac{1}{5} = 3 + \underline{\hspace{1cm}}$	$4\frac{1}{2} = \underline{\hspace{1cm}} + \frac{1}{2}$	$3\frac{3}{4} = \underline{\hspace{1cm}} + \underline{\hspace{1cm}}$	$9 + \frac{1}{3} = \underline{\hspace{1cm}}$
2.	$4\frac{2}{3} = 4 + \underline{\hspace{1cm}}$	$5\frac{3}{7} = \underline{\hspace{1cm}} + \frac{3}{7}$	$6\frac{2}{5} = \underline{\hspace{1cm}} + \underline{\hspace{1cm}}$	$8 + \frac{7}{8} = \underline{\hspace{1cm}}$
3.	$5\frac{1}{8} = 5 + \underline{\hspace{1cm}}$	$2\frac{1}{6} = \underline{\hspace{1cm}} + \frac{1}{6}$	$3\frac{1}{3} = \underline{\hspace{1cm}} + \underline{\hspace{1cm}}$	$5 + \frac{3}{7} = \underline{\hspace{1cm}}$

Change each fraction to a mixed numeral.

	a	*b*	*c*
4.	$\frac{5}{2}$	$\frac{9}{5}$	$\frac{7}{2}$
5.	$\frac{9}{4}$	$\frac{6}{5}$	$\frac{8}{3}$
6.	$\frac{14}{3}$	$\frac{10}{3}$	$\frac{17}{5}$

Tell whether each of the following is *less than 1, equal to 1,* or *greater than 1.*

	a	*b*	*c*
7.	$\frac{7}{8}$ _____	$\frac{5}{4}$ _____	$\frac{6}{6}$ _____
8.	$\frac{2}{3}$ _____	$\frac{12}{12}$ _____	$\frac{11}{10}$ _____
9.	$\frac{1}{9}$ _____	$\frac{12}{9}$ _____	$\frac{10}{5}$ _____

Addition

$\frac{2}{5}+\frac{1}{5}=\frac{2+1}{5}$ Add the numerators.

$\quad\quad=\frac{3}{5}$ Use the same denominator.

$\frac{3}{10}+\frac{4}{10}+\frac{2}{10}=\frac{\quad+\quad+\quad}{10}$

$\quad\quad\quad\quad=\frac{}{10}$

$\begin{array}{r}\frac{3}{10}\\\frac{4}{10}\\+\frac{2}{10}\\\hline\end{array}$

Add.

	a	*b*	*c*	*d*
1.	$\frac{3}{5}+\frac{1}{5}$	$\frac{4}{8}+\frac{3}{8}$	$\frac{2}{7}+\frac{2}{7}$	$\frac{1}{5}+\frac{2}{5}+\frac{1}{5}$
2.	$\frac{3}{6}+\frac{2}{6}$	$\frac{1}{7}+\frac{3}{7}$	$\frac{2}{8}+\frac{1}{8}$	$\frac{1}{4}+\frac{1}{4}+\frac{1}{4}$
3.	$\frac{3}{10}+\frac{4}{10}$	$\frac{4}{12}+\frac{1}{12}$	$\frac{5}{11}+\frac{4}{11}$	$\frac{2}{15}+\frac{2}{15}+\frac{7}{15}$

Add.

	a	*b*	*c*	*d*	*e*	*f*
4.	$\begin{array}{r}\frac{4}{6}\\+\frac{1}{6}\\\hline\end{array}$	$\begin{array}{r}\frac{3}{8}\\+\frac{4}{8}\\\hline\end{array}$	$\begin{array}{r}\frac{1}{7}\\+\frac{2}{7}\\\hline\end{array}$	$\begin{array}{r}\frac{3}{10}\\+\frac{6}{10}\\\hline\end{array}$	$\begin{array}{r}\frac{7}{12}\\+\frac{4}{12}\\\hline\end{array}$	$\begin{array}{r}\frac{3}{11}\\+\frac{1}{11}\\\hline\end{array}$
5.	$\begin{array}{r}\frac{1}{5}\\\frac{1}{5}\\+\frac{1}{5}\\\hline\end{array}$	$\begin{array}{r}\frac{2}{7}\\\frac{3}{7}\\+\frac{1}{7}\\\hline\end{array}$	$\begin{array}{r}\frac{2}{8}\\\frac{1}{8}\\+\frac{2}{8}\\\hline\end{array}$	$\begin{array}{r}\frac{4}{10}\\\frac{1}{10}\\+\frac{2}{10}\\\hline\end{array}$	$\begin{array}{r}\frac{3}{15}\\\frac{4}{15}\\+\frac{4}{15}\\\hline\end{array}$	$\begin{array}{r}\frac{1}{12}\\\frac{4}{12}\\+\frac{2}{12}\\\hline\end{array}$

Changing a Mixed Numeral to a Fraction

$4\frac{2}{3} = \frac{(3 \times 4) + 2}{3}$ Multiply the denominator by the whole number and add the numerator. $3\frac{1}{6} = \frac{(\times) +}{6}$

$= \frac{12 + 2}{3}$ Use the same denominator. $= \frac{+}{6}$

$= \frac{14}{3}$ $= \frac{}{6}$

Change each mixed numeral to a fraction.

	a	*b*	*c*
1.	$2\frac{5}{8}$	$2\frac{3}{5}$	$3\frac{2}{3}$
2.	$3\frac{7}{10}$	$10\frac{2}{3}$	$14\frac{1}{2}$
3.	$6\frac{7}{8}$	$5\frac{9}{10}$	$13\frac{5}{12}$
4.	$4\frac{5}{6}$	$7\frac{3}{4}$	$8\frac{11}{12}$

SPECTRUM MATHEMATICS,
Green Book–Second Edition

Perfect score: 12   My score: _____

Multiplication

Multiply the numerators.

$$\frac{2}{3} \times \frac{1}{5} = \frac{2 \times 1}{3 \times 5} = \frac{2}{15}$$

Multiply the denominators.

$$\frac{1}{2} \times \frac{3}{4} = \frac{1 \times 3}{2 \times 4}$$

$$= \frac{}{8}$$

$$\frac{2}{5} \times \frac{1}{3} = \frac{\times}{\times}$$

$$= \frac{}{}$$

Multiply.

	a	b	c	d
1.	$\frac{1}{2} \times \frac{1}{3}$	$\frac{3}{4} \times \frac{1}{2}$	$\frac{1}{3} \times \frac{1}{4}$	$\frac{3}{5} \times \frac{1}{2}$
2.	$\frac{3}{5} \times \frac{3}{4}$	$\frac{4}{7} \times \frac{3}{5}$	$\frac{4}{5} \times \frac{2}{3}$	$\frac{3}{8} \times \frac{5}{7}$
3.	$\frac{2}{3} \times \frac{4}{5}$	$\frac{1}{8} \times \frac{1}{2}$	$\frac{5}{7} \times \frac{3}{4}$	$\frac{3}{5} \times \frac{7}{8}$
4.	$\frac{6}{7} \times \frac{3}{5}$	$\frac{2}{9} \times \frac{1}{3}$	$\frac{5}{8} \times \frac{3}{7}$	$\frac{2}{7} \times \frac{3}{5}$
5.	$\frac{7}{8} \times \frac{7}{8}$	$\frac{2}{3} \times \frac{2}{3}$	$\frac{4}{9} \times \frac{2}{3}$	$\frac{4}{5} \times \frac{6}{7}$
6.	$\frac{8}{9} \times \frac{5}{7}$	$\frac{5}{8} \times \frac{1}{3}$	$\frac{5}{6} \times \frac{5}{7}$	$\frac{3}{8} \times \frac{5}{8}$

SPECTRUM MATHEMATICS,
Green Book–Second Edition

Perfect score: 24   My score: _____

Renaming Numbers

$4 = \dfrac{\boxed{}}{3}$

$\dfrac{1}{2} = \dfrac{\boxed{}}{10}$

$4 = \dfrac{4}{1}$ Name the whole number as a fraction.

$\dfrac{1}{2} = \dfrac{1 \times 5}{2 \times 5}$ ← Multiply the numerator and the denominator by the same number. → $= \dfrac{4 \times 3}{1 \times 3}$

$= \dfrac{5}{10}$ Use 5 so the new denominator is 10.

$= \dfrac{12}{3}$ Use 3 so the new denominator is 3.

Rename as shown.

	a	*b*	*c*	*d*
1.	$\dfrac{1}{2} = \dfrac{4}{8}$	$\dfrac{2}{3} = \dfrac{\boxed{}}{6}$	$\dfrac{4}{5} = \dfrac{\boxed{}}{10}$	$\dfrac{3}{4} = \dfrac{\boxed{}}{12}$
	$\dfrac{1}{2} = \dfrac{1 \times 4}{2 \times 4}$			
	$= \dfrac{4}{8}$			

2.	$3 = \dfrac{12}{4}$	$4 = \dfrac{\boxed{}}{6}$	$3 = \dfrac{\boxed{}}{10}$	$5 = \dfrac{\boxed{}}{5}$
	$\dfrac{3}{1} = \dfrac{3 \times 4}{1 \times 4}$			
	$= \dfrac{12}{4}$			

3.	$\dfrac{1}{2} = \dfrac{\boxed{}}{16}$	$10 = \dfrac{\boxed{}}{8}$	$\dfrac{5}{8} = \dfrac{\boxed{}}{16}$	$\dfrac{5}{6} = \dfrac{\boxed{}}{18}$

SPECTRUM MATHEMATICS,
Green Book–Second Edition

Perfect score: 10   My score: _____

Greatest Common Factor

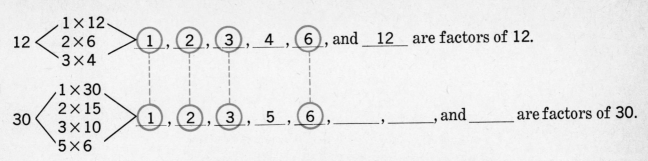

12 {
1 × 12
2 × 6
3 × 4
} → (1), (2), (3), 4 , (6), and 12 are factors of 12.

30 {
1 × 30
2 × 15
3 × 10
5 × 6
} → (1), (2), (3), 5 , (6), _____, _____, and _____ are factors of 30.

1, 2, 3, and 6 are **common factors** of 12 and 30.

6 is the **greatest common factor** of 12 and 30.

List the factors of each number named below. Then list the common factors and the greatest common factor of each pair of numbers.

		factors	*common factor(s)*	*greatest common factor*
1.	6	_____		
	10	_____	_____	_____
2.	5	_____		
	8	_____	_____	_____
3.	12	_____		
	15	_____	_____	_____
4.	10	_____		
	20	_____	_____	_____
5.	14	_____		
	16	_____	_____	_____
6.	15	_____		
	7	_____	_____	_____
7.	24	_____		
	18	_____	_____	_____

Fractions and Mixed Numerals in Simplest Form

A fraction is in simplest form when its numerator and denominator have no common factors, except 1.

Divide 12 and 15 by their greatest common factor.

$$\frac{12}{15} = \frac{12 \div 3}{15 \div 3} = \frac{4}{5}$$

The simplest form for $\frac{12}{15}$ is $\frac{4}{5}$.

A mixed numeral is in simplest form when its fraction is in simplest form and names a number less than 1.

Divide 4 and 6 by their greatest common factor.

$$3\frac{4}{6} = 3 + \frac{4 \div 2}{6 \div 2}$$
$$= 3 + \frac{2}{3}$$
$$= 3\frac{2}{3}$$

The simplest form for $3\frac{4}{6}$ is _____.

Change each of the following to simplest form.

	a	*b*	*c*
1.	$\frac{8}{10}$	$\frac{10}{20}$	$\frac{14}{21}$
2.	$2\frac{4}{8}$	$3\frac{6}{9}$	$5\frac{8}{10}$
3.	$\frac{12}{18}$	$5\frac{9}{12}$	$\frac{15}{18}$
4.	$6\frac{8}{12}$	$\frac{25}{30}$	$3\frac{12}{16}$
5.	$\frac{24}{30}$	$3\frac{14}{18}$	$\frac{16}{32}$

SPECTRUM MATHEMATICS,
Green Book–Second Edition

Perfect score: 15   My score: _____

Multiplication

$$\frac{1}{2} \times \frac{3}{4} = \frac{1 \times 3}{2 \times 4}$$
$$= \frac{3}{8}$$

Is $\frac{3}{8}$ in simplest form? _____

$$\frac{4}{5} \times \frac{1}{6} = \frac{4 \times 1}{5 \times 6}$$
$$= \frac{4}{30} \dashrightarrow \frac{4}{30} = \frac{4 \div 2}{30 \div 2}$$
$$= \frac{2}{15} \dashleftarrow = \frac{2}{15}$$

Is $\frac{4}{30}$ in simplest form? _____
Is $\frac{2}{15}$ in simplest form? _____

Write each answer in simplest form.

	a	*b*	*c*	*d*
1.	$\frac{1}{2} \times \frac{3}{5}$	$\frac{2}{3} \times \frac{4}{5}$	$\frac{2}{3} \times \frac{2}{3}$	$\frac{5}{6} \times \frac{1}{7}$
2.	$\frac{3}{4} \times \frac{4}{5}$	$\frac{5}{6} \times \frac{2}{3}$	$\frac{6}{7} \times \frac{2}{3}$	$\frac{3}{5} \times \frac{4}{9}$
3.	$\frac{5}{6} \times \frac{2}{5}$	$\frac{4}{5} \times \frac{5}{6}$	$\frac{3}{8} \times \frac{2}{3}$	$\frac{2}{10} \times \frac{5}{6}$
4.	$\frac{6}{5} \times \frac{3}{8}$	$\frac{9}{10} \times \frac{5}{12}$	$\frac{8}{9} \times \frac{3}{10}$	$\frac{5}{6} \times \frac{9}{10}$
5.	$\frac{4}{7} \times \frac{5}{6}$	$\frac{3}{8} \times \frac{7}{10}$	$\frac{9}{10} \times \frac{5}{9}$	$\frac{6}{7} \times \frac{9}{10}$

Problems

Solve. Write each answer in simplest form.

1. The Urbans had $\frac{3}{4}$ gallon of milk. One half of this was used for dinner. How much milk was used for dinner? ($\frac{1}{2}$ of $\frac{3}{4} = \frac{1}{2} \times \frac{3}{4}$)

_____ gallon was used for dinner.

2. Marsha read $\frac{4}{5}$ of a book. Two thirds of that reading was done at school. How much of the book did she read at school?

She read _____ of the book.

3. Tricia lives $\frac{4}{5}$ mile from school. One morning she ran $\frac{1}{2}$ of the distance to school. How far did Tricia run?

Tricia ran _____

4. Three fourths of a room has been painted. Joe did $\frac{2}{3}$ of the painting. How much of the room did Joe paint?

Joe painted _____

5. A truck was carrying $\frac{3}{4}$ ton of sand. One third of the sand was put into barrels. How much sand was put into barrels?

_____ ton of sand was put into barrels.

6. Carrie had a rope that was $\frac{2}{3}$ yard long. She used $\frac{1}{2}$ of it. How much rope did she use?

_____ yard of rope was used.

7. One fourth of the pupils in a class have blue eyes. Two thirds of the blue-eyed pupils have blond hair. What part of the class has blond hair and blue eyes?

_____ have blond hair and blue eyes.

1. _____

2. _____

3. _____

4. _____

5. _____

6. _____

7. _____

Multiplication

$$4 \times \frac{5}{6} = \frac{4}{1} \times \frac{5}{6}$$

Rename whole numbers and mixed numerals as fractions.

$$4\frac{2}{3} \times 5 = \frac{14}{3} \times \frac{5}{1}$$

$$= \frac{4 \times 5}{1 \times 6}$$

Multiply the fractions.

$$= \frac{14 \times 5}{3 \times 1}$$

$$= \frac{20}{6}$$

$$= \frac{70}{3}$$

$$= 3\frac{1}{3}$$

Change to simplest form.

$$= 23\frac{1}{3}$$

Write each answer in simplest form.

	a	b	c	d
1.	$5 \times \frac{2}{3}$	$6 \times \frac{4}{5}$	$\frac{1}{2} \times 9$	$\frac{3}{4} \times 7$
2.	$9 \times \frac{5}{6}$	$\frac{1}{4} \times 6$	$\frac{3}{8} \times 12$	$10 \times \frac{4}{5}$
3.	$2\frac{1}{2} \times 3$	$1\frac{1}{3} \times 5$	$2 \times 3\frac{2}{5}$	$4 \times 4\frac{2}{3}$

Perfect score: 12   My score: _____

Problems

Solve. Write each answer in simplest form.

1. A can of fruit weighs $\frac{2}{3}$ pound. How many pounds would 3 cans of fruit weigh?

1.

Three cans of fruit would weigh _____ pounds.

2. A plumber expects a job to take 10 hours. The plumber has already worked $\frac{4}{5}$ of that time. How many hours has the plumber worked?

2.

The plumber has worked _____ hours.

3. Each book is $\frac{7}{8}$ inch thick. How many inches high would a stack of 12 such books be?

3.

The stack would be _____ inches high.

4. The carpenter stacked 15 sheets of wall board on top of each other. If each sheet is $\frac{5}{8}$ inch thick, how high is the stack?

4.

The stack is _____ inches high.

5. Mark practiced the piano for $\frac{3}{4}$ hour on each of 4 days. How many hours did he practice in all?

5.

Mark practiced _____ hours in all.

6. Each class period lasts $\frac{5}{6}$ hour. How many hours are there in 6 class periods?

6.

There are _____ hours in 6 class periods.

7. Twenty-four pupils are in Mr. Roberts' class. Suppose $\frac{2}{3}$ of his class are girls. How many of his pupils are girls? How many are boys?

7.

_____ of his pupils are girls.

_____ of his pupils are boys.

Multiplication

$2\frac{3}{5} \times 1\frac{1}{6} = \frac{13}{5} \times \frac{7}{6}$ Change the mixed numerals to fractions.

$= \frac{13 \times 7}{5 \times 6}$ Multiply the fractions.

$= \frac{91}{30}$

$= 3\frac{1}{30}$ Change to simplest form.

Write each answer in simplest form.

	a	b	c	d
1.	$4\frac{2}{3} \times 1\frac{2}{5}$	$3\frac{1}{2} \times 1\frac{1}{6}$	$1\frac{2}{3} \times 2\frac{1}{2}$	$2\frac{2}{3} \times 2\frac{2}{3}$
2.	$2\frac{2}{5} \times 2\frac{1}{4}$	$1\frac{7}{10} \times 2\frac{1}{2}$	$5\frac{1}{3} \times 1\frac{1}{5}$	$2\frac{4}{5} \times 1\frac{1}{7}$
3.	$3\frac{3}{4} \times 2\frac{1}{3}$	$3\frac{2}{5} \times 1\frac{7}{8}$	$4\frac{2}{3} \times 1\frac{1}{8}$	$3\frac{3}{4} \times 3\frac{1}{3}$
4.	$5\frac{1}{6} \times 6\frac{3}{8}$	$2\frac{3}{5} \times 2\frac{1}{2}$	$1\frac{1}{4} \times 1\frac{1}{4}$	$3\frac{1}{8} \times 6\frac{2}{3}$

SPECTRUM MATHEMATICS,
Green Book–Second Edition

Perfect score: 16   My score: _____

Problems

Solve. Write each answer in simplest form.

1. A full box of soap weighs $2\frac{2}{3}$ pounds. How many pounds would $1\frac{1}{3}$ boxes of soap weigh?

They would weigh _____ pounds.

2. It takes $1\frac{4}{5}$ hours to process 1 ton of ore. How many hours would it take to process $3\frac{1}{3}$ tons of ore?

It would take _____ hours.

3. Each box of bolts weighs $3\frac{3}{4}$ pounds. How many pounds would $8\frac{1}{2}$ boxes of bolts weigh?

They would weigh _____ pounds.

4. The boys can walk $3\frac{1}{2}$ miles in 1 hour. At that rate, how many miles could the boys walk in $1\frac{1}{6}$ hours?

The boys could walk _____ miles.

5. Each bag of apples weighs $4\frac{1}{2}$ pounds. How much would $3\frac{1}{2}$ bags of apples weigh?

They would weigh _____ pounds.

6. Riding her bicycle, Terry averages $9\frac{1}{2}$ miles per hour. At that speed, how far could she go in $2\frac{2}{3}$ hours?

She could go _____ miles.

7. In problem **6**, suppose Terry averages $9\frac{3}{4}$ miles per hour. How far could she go in $2\frac{2}{3}$ hours?

She could go _____ miles.

8. A machine can process $2\frac{1}{2}$ tons in 1 hour. How many tons can the machine process in $2\frac{1}{10}$ hours?

The machine can process _____ tons in $2\frac{1}{10}$ hours.

9. If the machine in problem **8** broke down after $1\frac{1}{2}$ hours, how many tons would have been processed?

_____ tons would have been processed.

1.	
2.	
3.	
4.	
5.	
6.	
7.	
8.	
9.	

SPECTRUM MATHEMATICS,
Green Book–Second Edition

Perfect score: 9   My score: _____

TEST—Multiplication

Write each answer in simplest form

	a		c	d
1.	$\dfrac{1}{2} \times \dfrac{5}{6}$	$\dfrac{?}{8} \times \dfrac{5}{6}$	$\dfrac{2}{3} \times \dfrac{5}{7}$	$\dfrac{3}{8} \times \dfrac{3}{8}$
2.	$\dfrac{5}{9} \times \dfrac{6}{7}$	$\dfrac{7}{10} \times \dfrac{8}{9}$	$\dfrac{9}{10} \times \dfrac{5}{6}$	$\dfrac{5}{8} \times \dfrac{4}{5}$
3.	$2 \times \dfrac{3}{5}$	$6 \times \dfrac{5}{7}$	$\dfrac{1}{2} \times 8$	$\dfrac{5}{6} \times 8$
4.	$4 \times 3\dfrac{1}{3}$	$\dfrac{4}{5} \times 2$	$10 \times \dfrac{4}{5}$	$\dfrac{3}{8} \times 10$
5.	$3\dfrac{1}{3} \times 1\dfrac{1}{7}$	$1\dfrac{4}{5} \times 3\dfrac{1}{2}$	$2\dfrac{2}{3} \times 1\dfrac{1}{10}$	$2\dfrac{4}{5} \times 4\dfrac{1}{6}$

PRE-TEST—Addition and Subtraction

Write each answer in simplest form.

	a	*b*	*c*	*d*
1.	$\frac{3}{7}$ $+\frac{1}{7}$	$\frac{4}{9}$ $+\frac{2}{9}$	$\frac{7}{8}$ $-\frac{2}{8}$	$\frac{9}{10}$ $-\frac{3}{10}$
2.	$\frac{2}{3}$ $+\frac{1}{2}$	$\frac{4}{6}$ $+\frac{7}{12}$	$\frac{5}{6}$ $-\frac{3}{8}$	$\frac{9}{10}$ $-\frac{5}{8}$
3.	3 $-\frac{2}{5}$	1 $-\frac{7}{8}$	4 $3\frac{3}{5}$ $+\frac{5}{6}$	$\frac{1}{2}$ 3 $+\frac{2}{5}$
4.	$2\frac{3}{4}$ $+1\frac{1}{2}$	$\frac{7}{10}$ $+3\frac{7}{8}$	$5\frac{4}{9}$ $-1\frac{1}{3}$	$2\frac{7}{12}$ $-\frac{5}{6}$
5.	$5\frac{4}{9}$ $-3\frac{1}{6}$	$7\frac{2}{5}$ $-2\frac{9}{10}$	$2\frac{1}{2}$ $4\frac{1}{3}$ $+3\frac{2}{5}$	$4\frac{1}{2}$ $\frac{5}{6}$ $+3\frac{2}{3}$

Addition and Subtraction

$$\frac{7}{8}+\frac{5}{8}=\frac{7+5}{8}=\frac{12}{8}=1\frac{1}{2}$$

Use the same denominator.

$$\begin{array}{r} \frac{7}{8} \\ +\frac{5}{8} \\ \hline \frac{12}{8}=1\frac{1}{2} \end{array}$$

$$\frac{5}{6}-\frac{1}{6}=\frac{5-1}{6}=\frac{4}{6}=\frac{2}{3}$$

Use the same denominator.

$$\begin{array}{r} \frac{5}{6} \\ -\frac{1}{6} \\ \hline \frac{4}{6}=\frac{2}{3} \end{array}$$

------- Change to simplest form. -------→

Write each answer in simplest form.

	a	b	c	d	e
1.	$\frac{1}{5}$ $+\frac{2}{5}$	$\frac{4}{7}$ $+\frac{2}{7}$	$\frac{3}{4}$ $+\frac{2}{4}$	$\frac{5}{6}$ $+\frac{4}{6}$	$\frac{7}{8}$ $+\frac{7}{8}$
2.	$\frac{5}{6}$ $-\frac{4}{6}$	$\frac{7}{8}$ $-\frac{3}{8}$	$\frac{5}{7}$ $-\frac{2}{7}$	$\frac{9}{9}$ $-\frac{4}{9}$	$\frac{5}{8}$ $-\frac{1}{8}$
3.	$\frac{3}{10}$ $+\frac{6}{10}$	$\frac{8}{9}$ $+\frac{4}{9}$	$\frac{3}{8}$ $+\frac{3}{8}$	$\frac{5}{12}$ $+\frac{5}{12}$	$\frac{10}{15}$ $+\frac{14}{15}$
4.	$\frac{11}{12}$ $-\frac{3}{12}$	$\frac{7}{8}$ $-\frac{2}{8}$	$\frac{8}{9}$ $-\frac{5}{9}$	$\frac{9}{10}$ $-\frac{4}{10}$	$\frac{9}{16}$ $-\frac{3}{16}$
5.	$\frac{7}{12}$ $+\frac{8}{12}$	$\frac{5}{9}$ $-\frac{2}{9}$	$\frac{8}{15}$ $+\frac{10}{15}$	$\frac{7}{10}$ $-\frac{3}{10}$	$\frac{6}{14}$ $+\frac{6}{14}$

Problems

Solve. Write each answer in simplest form.

1. Walter drank $\frac{1}{4}$ gallon of milk yesterday and $\frac{1}{4}$ gallon of milk today. What part of a gallon of milk did he drink during these two days?

He drank _____ gallon of milk.

2. Trina and Trudy have painted $\frac{3}{4}$ of a room. Trudy painted $\frac{1}{4}$ of the room. How much of the room did Trina paint?

Trina painted _____ of the room.

3. Tom measured two boards. He found that each was $\frac{3}{8}$ inch thick. What would be the total thickness of the boards if he glues them together?

The total thickness would be _____ inch.

4. An unopened box of cereal weighed $\frac{15}{16}$ pound. Mother used $\frac{5}{16}$ pound of cereal from the box. How much cereal remains in the box?

_____ pound remains in the box.

5. A class period has just begun and will last $\frac{5}{6}$ hour. After $\frac{4}{6}$ hour, what part of an hour remains in the period?

_____ hour remains in the period.

6. Helen practiced the guitar $\frac{3}{4}$ hour in the morning and $\frac{3}{4}$ hour in the afternoon. How long did Helen practice the guitar?

She practiced _____ hours.

7. Jerry spent $\frac{5}{6}$ hour studying spelling and $\frac{1}{6}$ hour studying history. How much time did he spend studying spelling and history?

He spent _____ hour studying.

8. In problem 7, how much longer did he spend studying spelling than studying history?

He spent _____ hour more studying spelling.

1.	2.
3.	4.
5.	6.
7.	8.

Addition and Subtraction

$$\frac{2}{3} \quad \begin{array}{c}\times 2 \\ \times 2\end{array} = \quad \frac{4}{6}$$
$$+\frac{1}{2} \quad \begin{array}{c}\times 3 \\ \times 3\end{array} = \quad +\frac{3}{6}$$
$$\frac{7}{6} = 1\frac{1}{6}$$

The denominators are 3 and 2.
Since $2 \times 3 = 6$, rename each
fraction with a denominator of 6.

Add or subtract the fractions.

Write the answer in simplest form.

$$\frac{2}{3} \quad \begin{array}{c}\times 2 \\ \times 2\end{array} = \quad \frac{4}{6}$$
$$-\frac{1}{2} \quad \begin{array}{c}\times 3 \\ \times 3\end{array} = \quad -\frac{3}{6}$$
$$\frac{1}{6}$$

Write each answer in simplest form.

	a	b	c	d
1.	$\frac{3}{5}$ $+\frac{2}{3}$	$\frac{5}{6}$ $+\frac{1}{5}$	$\frac{1}{2}$ $+\frac{1}{3}$	$\frac{3}{10}$ $+\frac{1}{3}$
2.	$\frac{2}{3}$ $-\frac{1}{4}$	$\frac{5}{6}$ $-\frac{2}{5}$	$\frac{7}{8}$ $-\frac{2}{3}$	$\frac{3}{4}$ $-\frac{1}{3}$
3.	$\frac{7}{8}$ $+\frac{1}{3}$	$\frac{7}{8}$ $-\frac{1}{3}$	$\frac{2}{5}$ $+\frac{3}{4}$	$\frac{1}{2}$ $-\frac{1}{3}$
4.	$\frac{1}{3}$ $+\frac{3}{4}$	$\frac{3}{5}$ $-\frac{1}{3}$	$\frac{1}{2}$ $+\frac{4}{5}$	$\frac{3}{4}$ $-\frac{2}{3}$

Addition and Subtraction

$$\frac{3}{4} \quad \overset{\times 3}{\times 3} \quad \frac{9}{12}$$
$$+\frac{1}{6} \quad \overset{\times 2}{\times 2} \quad +\frac{2}{12}$$
$$\overline{} \qquad \qquad \overline{\frac{11}{12}}$$

The denominators are 4 and 6. Since $3 \times 4 = 12$ and $2 \times 6 = 12$, rename each fraction with a denominator of 12.

Add the fractions.

$$\frac{9}{10} \longrightarrow \frac{9}{10}$$
$$-\frac{2}{5} \quad \overset{\times 2}{\times 2} \quad -\frac{4}{10}$$
$$\overline{} \qquad \qquad \overline{\frac{5}{10} = \frac{1}{2}}$$

The denominators are 5 and 10. Since $2 \times 5 = 10$, rename only $\frac{2}{5}$ with a denominator of 10. Subtract the fractions.

Change to simplest form.

Write each answer in simplest form.

	a	b	c	d
1.	$\frac{2}{5}$ $+\frac{1}{2}$	$\frac{2}{5}$ $+\frac{1}{3}$	$\frac{3}{4}$ $+\frac{1}{2}$	$\frac{7}{8}$ $+\frac{1}{4}$
2.	$\frac{2}{3}$ $-\frac{1}{4}$	$\frac{3}{5}$ $-\frac{1}{2}$	$\frac{2}{3}$ $-\frac{1}{6}$	$\frac{1}{2}$ $-\frac{3}{10}$
3.	$\frac{9}{10}$ $+\frac{1}{2}$	$\frac{5}{6}$ $-\frac{3}{4}$	$\frac{5}{6}$ $+\frac{1}{2}$	$\frac{7}{10}$ $-\frac{1}{5}$
4.	$\frac{2}{3}$ $+\frac{5}{6}$	$\frac{11}{12}$ $-\frac{1}{4}$	$\frac{5}{6}$ $+\frac{3}{10}$	$\frac{9}{10}$ $-\frac{1}{2}$

SPECTRUM MATHEMATICS,
Green Book—Second Edition

Perfect score: 16   My score: _____

Addition

$3\frac{1}{2}$ ⟶ $3\frac{4}{8}$
$+1\frac{1}{8}$ ⟶ $+1\frac{1}{8}$
$4\frac{5}{8}$

Rename the numbers so
the fractions have the
same denominator.
Add the fractions.
Add the whole numbers.
Change to simplest form.

$1\frac{1}{2}$ ⟶ $1\frac{6}{12}$
$3\frac{3}{4}$ ⟶ $3\frac{9}{12}$
$+\frac{2}{3}$ ⟶ $+\frac{8}{12}$
$4\frac{23}{12} = 5\frac{11}{12}$

Write each answer in simplest form.

	a	b	c	d
1.	$3\frac{1}{4}$ $+2\frac{4}{5}$	$3\frac{1}{6}$ $+\frac{3}{4}$	$5\frac{1}{2}$ $+1\frac{5}{8}$	$3\frac{11}{12}$ $+\frac{5}{6}$
2.	$9\frac{7}{8}$ $+\frac{3}{4}$	$7\frac{2}{5}$ $+4\frac{3}{10}$	$\frac{3}{5}$ $+2\frac{5}{6}$	$\frac{9}{10}$ $+3\frac{5}{6}$
3.	$6\frac{2}{3}$ $1\frac{3}{4}$ $+\frac{1}{6}$	$2\frac{1}{5}$ $2\frac{1}{4}$ $+1\frac{1}{2}$	$3\frac{1}{3}$ $\frac{5}{6}$ $+3\frac{7}{12}$	$\frac{1}{2}$ $5\frac{1}{5}$ $+1\frac{3}{10}$
4.	$\frac{3}{5}$ $1\frac{2}{3}$ $+2\frac{1}{2}$	$3\frac{5}{8}$ $2\frac{1}{6}$ $+\frac{5}{12}$	$\frac{1}{4}$ $1\frac{1}{2}$ $+4\frac{7}{8}$	$2\frac{2}{3}$ $2\frac{1}{2}$ $+3\frac{2}{5}$

Subtraction

$$3\frac{2}{3} \longrightarrow 3\frac{4}{6}$$
$$-1\frac{1}{6} \longrightarrow -1\frac{1}{6}$$
$$\overline{\qquad\qquad 2\frac{3}{6}=2\frac{1}{2}}$$

Rename the numbers so the
fractions have the same
denominator.
Subtract the fractions.
Subtract the whole numbers.

Change to simplest form.

$$3 \longrightarrow 2\frac{4}{4}$$
$$-\frac{1}{4} \longrightarrow -\frac{1}{4}$$
$$\overline{\qquad\qquad 2\frac{3}{4}}$$

$$3 = 2 + 1$$
$$= 2 + \frac{4}{4}$$
$$= 2\frac{4}{4}$$

Write each answer in simplest form.

	a	*b*	*c*	*d*
1.	7 $-\frac{3}{4}$	4 $-\frac{1}{2}$	5 $-\frac{2}{3}$	8 $-\frac{1}{8}$
2.	$3\frac{4}{5}$ $-1\frac{1}{2}$	$5\frac{2}{3}$ $-3\frac{4}{9}$	$4\frac{5}{6}$ $-1\frac{1}{2}$	$5\frac{9}{10}$ $-3\frac{2}{5}$
3.	5 $-\frac{3}{5}$	$6\frac{3}{4}$ $-5\frac{1}{8}$	$2\frac{2}{3}$ $-1\frac{1}{2}$	10 $-2\frac{3}{10}$
4.	$10\frac{5}{6}$ $-7\frac{5}{12}$	8 $-\frac{5}{8}$	$9\frac{5}{6}$ $-2\frac{1}{3}$	6 $-\frac{9}{10}$

Subtraction

Rename the numbers so the fractions have the same denominator.

Rename $3\frac{3}{12}$ so you can subtract the fractions.

$$3\frac{1}{4} \rightarrow 3\frac{3}{12} \rightarrow 2\frac{15}{12}$$
$$-1\frac{5}{6} \rightarrow -1\frac{10}{12} \rightarrow -1\frac{10}{12}$$
$$\phantom{-1\frac{10}{12}} \qquad 1\frac{5}{12}$$

$$3\frac{3}{12} = 2 + 1\frac{3}{12}$$
$$= 2 + \frac{15}{12}$$
$$= 2\frac{15}{12}$$

Rename $4\frac{5}{10}$ so you can subtract the fractions.

$$4\frac{1}{2} \rightarrow 4\frac{5}{10} \rightarrow 3\frac{15}{10}$$
$$-1\frac{3}{5} \rightarrow -1\frac{6}{10} \rightarrow -1\frac{6}{10}$$
$$\phantom{-1\frac{6}{10}} \qquad 2\frac{9}{10}$$

$$4\frac{5}{10} = 3 + 1\frac{5}{10}$$
$$= 3 + \frac{15}{10}$$
$$= 3\frac{15}{10}$$

Write each answer in simplest form.

	a	b	c	d
1.	$2\frac{1}{2}$ $-1\frac{3}{4}$	$5\frac{1}{4}$ $-4\frac{1}{3}$	$7\frac{3}{4}$ $-3\frac{5}{6}$	$6\frac{2}{5}$ $-4\frac{1}{2}$
2.	$8\frac{3}{8}$ $-1\frac{7}{8}$	$5\frac{1}{4}$ $-4\frac{3}{4}$	$3\frac{7}{12}$ $-1\frac{3}{4}$	$4\frac{1}{6}$ $-2\frac{3}{8}$
3.	$9\frac{1}{2}$ $-5\frac{7}{10}$	$6\frac{1}{3}$ $-3\frac{5}{6}$	$11\frac{1}{6}$ $-4\frac{5}{12}$	$3\frac{3}{10}$ $-2\frac{1}{2}$
4.	$7\frac{3}{4}$ $-5\frac{4}{5}$	$12\frac{1}{4}$ $-6\frac{5}{8}$	$15\frac{1}{2}$ $-8\frac{2}{3}$	$10\frac{1}{6}$ $-3\frac{3}{4}$

Problems

Solve. Write each answer in simplest form.

1. A record has been playing for $\frac{1}{3}$ hour. The record still has $\frac{1}{12}$ hour to play. What is the total length of time the record can play?

The record can play _____ hour.

2. It rained $\frac{3}{4}$ inch yesterday and $\frac{3}{10}$ inch today. How much more did it rain yesterday?

It rained _____ inch more yesterday.

3. Jim spent $\frac{1}{2}$ hour doing his history homework and $\frac{3}{4}$ hour doing his science homework. How much time did he spend doing homework?

He spent _____ hours doing homework.

4. Bob has a board that is $\frac{1}{8}$ inch too wide. The board is $\frac{3}{4}$ inch wide. What width board does Bob need?

Bob needs a board _____ inch wide.

5. Shirley read $\frac{3}{5}$ hour in the morning and $\frac{1}{2}$ hour in the afternoon. How many hours did she read in the morning and afternoon?

She read _____ hours.

6. In problem 5, how much longer did she read in the morning than in the afternoon?

She read _____ hour longer in the morning.

7. John has two boxes. One weighs $\frac{3}{10}$ pound and the other weighs $\frac{7}{8}$ pound. What is the combined weight of both boxes?

The combined weight is _____ pounds.

8. In problem 7, how much more does the heavier box weigh?

The heavier box weighs _____ pound more.

1.
2.
3.
4.
5.
6.
7.
8.

Addition and Subtraction

Write each answer in simplest form.

	a	b	c	d
1.	$\dfrac{7}{8}$ $+\dfrac{5}{8}$	$\dfrac{9}{16}$ $-\dfrac{3}{16}$	$\dfrac{3}{5}$ $+\dfrac{2}{5}$	$\dfrac{11}{12}$ $-\dfrac{3}{12}$
2.	$\dfrac{1}{2}$ $+\dfrac{7}{8}$	$\dfrac{4}{5}$ $-\dfrac{2}{3}$	$\dfrac{4}{9}$ $+\dfrac{5}{6}$	$\dfrac{3}{4}$ $-\dfrac{5}{12}$
3.	9 $-\dfrac{5}{9}$	1 $-\dfrac{3}{10}$	4 $\dfrac{3}{8}$ $+\dfrac{3}{4}$	$\dfrac{7}{12}$ $\dfrac{2}{3}$ $+7$
4.	$\dfrac{2}{3}$ $+3\dfrac{4}{5}$	$7\dfrac{3}{8}$ $-\dfrac{2}{3}$	$6\dfrac{1}{6}$ $+\dfrac{5}{12}$	$1\dfrac{2}{5}$ $-\dfrac{7}{10}$
5.	$14\dfrac{3}{4}$ $-3\dfrac{11}{12}$	$16\dfrac{11}{12}$ $-2\dfrac{1}{6}$	$3\dfrac{2}{3}$ $2\dfrac{1}{5}$ $+4\dfrac{3}{8}$	$2\dfrac{5}{6}$ $3\dfrac{1}{5}$ $+2\dfrac{3}{10}$

Problems

Rock	Weight
A	$\frac{7}{8}$ pound
B	$1\frac{1}{4}$ pounds
C	3 pounds
D	$2\frac{7}{10}$ pounds

Solve. Write each answer in simplest form.

1. The pupils put rocks A and B on the scales. What is the combined weight of both rocks?

2. How much more does rock B weigh than rock A?

3. What is the combined weight of rocks B and C?

4. Considering rocks A and C, how much more does the heavier rock weigh?

5. What is the combined weight of rocks A, B, and C?

6. What is the combined weight of rocks A, B, and D?

7. How much less does rock C weigh than the combined weight of rocks B and D?

1.

2.

3.

4.

5.

6.

7.

SPECTRUM MATHEMATICS,
Green Book–Second Edition

Perfect score: 7   My score: _____

TEST—Addition and Subtraction

answer in simplest form.

	a	b	c	d
1.	$\dfrac{3}{8}$ $+\dfrac{4}{8}$	$\dfrac{7}{10}$ $-\dfrac{2}{10}$	$\dfrac{5}{12}$ $+\dfrac{9}{12}$	$\dfrac{8}{9}$ $-\dfrac{6}{9}$
2.	$\dfrac{5}{6}$ $+\dfrac{2}{9}$	$\dfrac{7}{8}$ $+\dfrac{1}{3}$	$\dfrac{9}{10}$ $-\dfrac{2}{5}$	$\dfrac{3}{4}$ $-\dfrac{2}{3}$
3.	6 $-\dfrac{1}{9}$	3 $-\dfrac{4}{7}$	$\dfrac{3}{8}$ $\dfrac{5}{6}$ $+4$	$\dfrac{7}{8}$ 2 $+\dfrac{3}{4}$
4.	$4\dfrac{5}{6}$ $+\dfrac{3}{5}$	$\dfrac{3}{8}$ $+2\dfrac{9}{10}$	$6\dfrac{3}{8}$ $-\dfrac{5}{6}$	$7\dfrac{1}{4}$ $-\dfrac{7}{12}$
5.	$6\dfrac{3}{5}$ $-2\dfrac{3}{4}$	$4\dfrac{5}{8}$ $-1\dfrac{1}{2}$	$9\dfrac{1}{8}$ $2\dfrac{4}{6}$ $+\dfrac{7}{10}$	$5\dfrac{3}{4}$ $\dfrac{1}{6}$ $+5\dfrac{3}{8}$

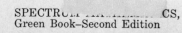

PRE-TEST—Division

Write each answer in simplest form.

	a	*b*	*c*	*d*
1.	$4 \div \frac{1}{2}$	$7 \div \frac{2}{3}$	$8 \div \frac{4}{5}$	$9 \div \frac{6}{7}$
2.	$\frac{1}{4} \div 2$	$\frac{3}{5} \div 2$	$\frac{3}{7} \div 3$	$\frac{8}{9} \div 6$
3.	$\frac{1}{7} \div \frac{1}{2}$	$\frac{1}{8} \div \frac{1}{4}$	$\frac{1}{4} \div \frac{1}{8}$	$\frac{1}{6} \div \frac{1}{7}$
4.	$\frac{1}{8} \div \frac{1}{10}$	$\frac{3}{5} \div \frac{2}{3}$	$\frac{4}{7} \div \frac{2}{7}$	$\frac{5}{6} \div \frac{5}{8}$
5.	$7\frac{1}{2} \div 10$	$3 \div 1\frac{1}{5}$	$\frac{1}{4} \div 1\frac{1}{6}$	$2\frac{1}{2} \div 1\frac{1}{6}$

SPECTRUM MATHEMATICS,
Green Book—Second Edition

Perfect score: 20   My score: _____

Reciprocals

The product of any number and its **reciprocal** is 1.

reciprocals

$$\frac{2}{3} \times \frac{3}{2} = \frac{2 \times 3}{3 \times 2} = \frac{6}{6} = 1$$

The reciprocal of $\frac{2}{3}$ is $\frac{3}{2}$.

The reciprocal of $\frac{3}{2}$ is ____.

reciprocals

$$\frac{1}{2} \times \frac{2}{1} = \frac{1 \times 2}{2 \times 1} = \frac{2}{2} = 1$$

The reciprocal of $\frac{1}{2}$ is $\frac{2}{1}$ or 2.

The reciprocal of 2 is ____.

Write the reciprocal of each of the following.

	a	b	c	d	e	f
1.	$\frac{3}{5}$ ____	$\frac{7}{8}$ ____	$\frac{4}{5}$ ____	$\frac{5}{7}$ ____	$\frac{4}{9}$ ____	$\frac{6}{7}$ ____
2.	$\frac{5}{3}$ ____	$\frac{8}{7}$ ____	$\frac{5}{4}$ ____	$\frac{7}{5}$ ____	$\frac{9}{4}$ ____	$\frac{7}{6}$ ____
3.	$\frac{1}{8}$ ____	$\frac{1}{3}$ ____	$\frac{1}{4}$ ____	$\frac{1}{9}$ ____	$\frac{1}{16}$ ____	$\frac{1}{14}$ ____
4.	$\frac{8}{1}$ ____	$\frac{3}{1}$ ____	$\frac{4}{1}$ ____	$\frac{9}{1}$ ____	$\frac{16}{1}$ ____	$\frac{14}{1}$ ____
5.	8 ____	3 ____	4 ____	9 ____	16 ____	14 ____
6.	$\frac{8}{5}$ ____	6 ____	$\frac{2}{3}$ ____	$\frac{11}{6}$ ____	$\frac{7}{4}$ ____	12 ____
7.	15 ____	$\frac{10}{9}$ ____	$\frac{12}{11}$ ____	17 ____	$\frac{8}{9}$ ____	$\frac{17}{2}$ ____
8.	$\frac{15}{8}$ ____	$\frac{5}{12}$ ____	11 ____	$\frac{7}{11}$ ____	$\frac{1}{11}$ ____	$\frac{17}{3}$ ____
9.	$\frac{10}{1}$ ____	13 ____	$\frac{1}{17}$ ____	$\frac{5}{11}$ ____	$\frac{9}{7}$ ____	5 ____
10.	$\frac{5}{8}$ ____	$\frac{1}{6}$ ____	7 ____	$\frac{12}{7}$ ____	2 ____	$\frac{2}{5}$ ____

Division

$$15 \div \tfrac{3}{4} = \tfrac{15}{1} \times \tfrac{4}{3}$$
$$= \tfrac{15 \times 4}{1 \times 3}$$
$$= \tfrac{60}{3}$$
$$= 20$$

To divide by a fraction, multiply by its reciprocal.

Multiply the fractions.

Write the answer in simplest form.

$$10 \div \tfrac{6}{7} = \tfrac{10}{1} \times \tfrac{7}{6}$$
$$= \tfrac{10 \times 7}{1 \times 6}$$
$$= \tfrac{70}{6}$$
$$= 11 \tfrac{2}{3}$$

Write each answer in simplest form.

	a	*b*	*c*	*d*
1.	$10 \div \tfrac{1}{3}$	$8 \div \tfrac{1}{2}$	$7 \div \tfrac{1}{4}$	$6 \div \tfrac{1}{5}$
2.	$14 \div \tfrac{2}{7}$	$15 \div \tfrac{2}{5}$	$16 \div \tfrac{3}{8}$	$18 \div \tfrac{5}{9}$
3.	$18 \div \tfrac{1}{3}$	$14 \div \tfrac{7}{8}$	$17 \div \tfrac{1}{2}$	$12 \div \tfrac{3}{4}$

SPECTRUM MATHEMATICS,
Green Book–Second Edition

Perfect score: 12   My score: _____

Division

$\frac{1}{2} \div 4 = \frac{1}{2} \times \frac{1}{4}$

$= \frac{1 \times 1}{2 \times 4}$

$= \frac{1}{8}$

To divide by a whole number, multiply by its reciprocal.

Multiply the fractions.

$\frac{2}{3} \div 5 = \frac{2}{3} \times \frac{1}{5}$

$= \frac{2 \times 1}{3 \times 5}$

$= \frac{2}{15}$

To divide $\frac{1}{2}$ by 4,

multiply $\frac{1}{2}$ by _____.

To divide $\frac{2}{3}$ by 5,

multiply $\frac{2}{3}$ by _____.

Write each answer in simplest form.

	a	b	c	d
1.	$\frac{1}{2} \div 6$	$\frac{1}{4} \div 2$	$\frac{1}{3} \div 5$	$\frac{1}{6} \div 2$
2.	$\frac{3}{5} \div 4$	$\frac{5}{8} \div 2$	$\frac{3}{4} \div 4$	$\frac{5}{6} \div 3$
3.	$\frac{3}{4} \div 6$	$\frac{2}{3} \div 6$	$\frac{4}{5} \div 4$	$\frac{5}{6} \div 10$

Problems

Solve. Write each answer in simplest form.

1. One third pound of flour is separated into 2 bowls. The same amount of flour is in each bowl. How much flour is in each bowl?

_____ pound is in each bowl.

2. One half of a room is painted. Each of 4 people did the same amount of painting. How much of the room did each person paint?

Each person painted _____ of the room.

3. Kevin used $\frac{3}{4}$ gallon of gasoline to mow a lawn 3 times. How much gasoline did he use to mow the lawn once?

_____ gallon was used.

4. A string $\frac{2}{3}$ yard long is cut into 4 pieces. Each piece is the same length. How long is each piece?

Each piece is _____ yard long.

5. Seven eighths gallon of liquid is poured into 4 containers. Each container has the same amount in it. How much liquid is in each container?

_____ gallon is in each container.

6. The pupils have $\frac{1}{2}$ hour to complete 3 sections of a quiz. They have the same amount of time to do each section. How much time do they have for each section of the quiz?

They have _____ hour to do each section.

1.
2.
3.
4.
5.
6.

Division

Multiply by
the reciprocal.

$$\frac{1}{4} \div \frac{1}{3} = \frac{1}{4} \times \frac{3}{1}$$
$$= \frac{1 \times 3}{4 \times 1}$$
$$= \frac{3}{4}$$

Multiply by
the reciprocal.

$$\frac{3}{4} \div \frac{1}{2} = \frac{3}{4} \times \frac{2}{1}$$
$$= \frac{3 \times 2}{4 \times 1}$$
$$= \frac{6}{4}$$
$$= 1\frac{2}{4}$$
$$= 1\frac{1}{2}$$

Write each answer in simplest form.

	a	b	c	d
1.	$\frac{1}{5} \div \frac{1}{2}$	$\frac{1}{3} \div \frac{1}{2}$	$\frac{1}{8} \div \frac{1}{4}$	$\frac{1}{9} \div \frac{1}{6}$
2.	$\frac{3}{5} \div \frac{1}{2}$	$\frac{4}{7} \div \frac{2}{3}$	$\frac{4}{5} \div \frac{1}{10}$	$\frac{5}{6} \div \frac{2}{3}$
3.	$\frac{4}{5} \div \frac{2}{5}$	$\frac{3}{8} \div \frac{3}{4}$	$\frac{4}{9} \div \frac{1}{5}$	$\frac{7}{8} \div \frac{7}{10}$

Perfect score: 12   My score: _____

Problems

Solve. Write each answer in simplest form.

1. How many $\frac{1}{6}$-hour sessions are there in $\frac{1}{2}$ hour?

There are _____ sessions.

2. Millie has a ribbon $\frac{3}{4}$ yard long. How many $\frac{1}{4}$-yard pieces can she get from her ribbon?

She can get _____ pieces.

3. In problem 2, how many $\frac{1}{8}$-yard pieces can Millie get from her ribbon?

She can get _____ pieces.

4. A machine uses gas at the rate of $\frac{1}{5}$ gallon an hour. So far $\frac{9}{10}$ gallon has been used. How many hours has the machine operated?

The machine operated _____ hours.

5. Suppose the machine in problem 4 has used $\frac{4}{5}$ gallon of gas. How many hours did the machine operate?

The machine operated _____ hours.

6. Three eighths pound of nuts is put in each bag. How many bags can be filled with $\frac{3}{4}$ pound of nuts?

_____ bags can be filled.

7. Wilbur walked $\frac{5}{6}$ hour. He walked at the rate of 1 mile every $\frac{1}{6}$ hour. How many miles did he walk?

He walked _____ miles.

8. Suppose in problem 7 Wilbur walked 1 mile every $\frac{5}{12}$ hour. How many miles did he walk?

He walked _____ miles.

9. A bell rings every $\frac{1}{6}$ hour. Assume it just rang. How many times will it ring in the next $\frac{2}{3}$ hour?

It will ring _____ times.

1.	
2.	
3.	
4.	
5.	
6.	
7.	
8.	
9.	

SPECTRUM MATHEMATICS,
Green Book–Second Edition

Perfect score: 9   My score: _____

Division

Write each answer in simplest form.

	a	b	c	d
1.	$8 \div \dfrac{2}{3}$	$\dfrac{4}{7} \div 5$	$\dfrac{1}{6} \div \dfrac{1}{3}$	$\dfrac{3}{5} \div \dfrac{2}{3}$
2.	$\dfrac{1}{8} \div \dfrac{1}{10}$	$6 \div \dfrac{1}{4}$	$\dfrac{1}{3} \div 2$	$\dfrac{1}{7} \div \dfrac{1}{3}$
3.	$\dfrac{1}{2} \div \dfrac{1}{5}$	$\dfrac{9}{10} \div \dfrac{4}{5}$	$9 \div \dfrac{3}{5}$	$\dfrac{4}{9} \div 6$
4.	$\dfrac{3}{5} \div 3$	$\dfrac{1}{3} \div \dfrac{1}{6}$	$\dfrac{3}{8} \div \dfrac{3}{10}$	$6 \div \dfrac{4}{5}$
5.	$\dfrac{7}{8} \div \dfrac{7}{8}$	$\dfrac{6}{7} \div \dfrac{8}{9}$	$7 \div \dfrac{1}{3}$	$\dfrac{6}{7} \div 4$

Problems

Solve. Write each answer in simplest form.

1. It takes $\frac{1}{3}$ hour to produce 1 woomble. How many woombles could be produced in 9 hours?

_____ woombles could be produced.

2. A rope $\frac{3}{4}$ yard long is cut into 9 pieces. Each piece is the same length. How long is each piece?

Each piece is _____ yard long.

3. Each class period is $\frac{3}{5}$ hour long. How many topics can be covered in 1 class period if it takes $\frac{3}{10}$ hour to cover each topic?

_____ topics can be covered.

4. Eight pounds of raisins are put in boxes. How many boxes are needed if $\frac{2}{3}$ pound of raisins is put into each box?

_____ boxes are needed.

5. Michelle and her 5 friends want to share $\frac{3}{4}$ pound of salami equally. How much salami will each person get?

Each person will get _____ pound.

6. A wire $4\frac{1}{2}$ feet long is cut into 9 pieces of the same length. How long is each piece?

Each piece is _____ foot long.

7. Three fourths gallon of milk is poured into 12 glasses. The same amount is in each glass. How much milk is in each glass?

_____ gallon is in each glass.

8. Mr. Roe has $\frac{9}{10}$ pound of a chemical to put into 6 tubes. Assume he puts the same amount in each tube. How many pounds of chemical will be in each tube?

_____ pound will be in each tube.

1.

2.

3.

4.

5.

6.

7.

8.

Division

$$2\frac{1}{5} \div 4 = \frac{11}{5} \div 4 \qquad \text{Change the mixed numerals to fractions.} \qquad 3\frac{1}{2} \div 1\frac{1}{2} = \frac{7}{2} \div \frac{3}{2}$$

$$= \frac{11}{5} \times \frac{1}{4} \qquad \text{To divide, multiply by the reciprocal.} \qquad = \frac{7}{2} \times \frac{2}{3}$$

$$= \frac{11}{20} \qquad \text{Multiply the fractions.} \qquad = \frac{14}{6}$$

$$\text{Write the answer in simplest form.} \qquad = 2\frac{1}{3}$$

Write each answer in simplest form.

	a	*b*	*c*	*d*
1.	$2\frac{1}{2} \div 3$	$1\frac{2}{5} \div 3$	$4 \div 1\frac{1}{3}$	$6 \div 1\frac{1}{3}$
2.	$1\frac{2}{7} \div 2\frac{1}{2}$	$1\frac{1}{5} \div 2\frac{2}{3}$	$4\frac{1}{2} \div 1\frac{1}{5}$	$1\frac{4}{5} \div 1\frac{1}{5}$
3.	$1\frac{4}{5} \div \frac{2}{7}$	$\frac{1}{6} \div 1\frac{1}{2}$	$3\frac{3}{5} \div 10$	$1\frac{1}{3} \div 2\frac{1}{2}$

Problems

Solve. Write each answer in simplest form.

1. Five pounds of sand are put into containers. How many containers are needed if $1\frac{1}{4}$ pounds of sand are put into each one?

_____ containers are needed.

1.

2. Yvonne works $1\frac{1}{2}$ hours each day. How many days will it take her to work 15 hours?

It will take _____ days.

2.

3. Each class period is $\frac{5}{6}$ hour long. How many periods can there be in $2\frac{1}{2}$ hours?

There can be _____ periods in $2\frac{1}{2}$ hours.

3.

4. The city spread $7\frac{1}{2}$ tons of salt on the streets. There were $1\frac{1}{4}$ tons on each load. How many loads of salt were spread on the streets?

_____ loads of salt were spread.

4.

5. It takes $1\frac{5}{6}$ hours to assemble a lawn mower. How many lawn mowers could be assembled in $16\frac{1}{2}$ hours?

_____ lawn mowers could be assembled.

5.

6. How many $1\frac{1}{2}$-hour practice sessions are there in 6 hours?

There are _____ practice sessions.

6.

7. How many $1\frac{3}{4}$-hour practice sessions are there in $10\frac{1}{2}$ hours?

There are _____ practice sessions.

7.

SPECTRUM MATHEMATICS,
Green Book–Second Edition

Perfect score: 7   My score: _____

TEST—Division

Write each answer in simplest form.

a	b	c	d
1. $5 \div \frac{1}{3}$	$8 \div \frac{3}{4}$	$4 \div \frac{2}{3}$	$10 \div \frac{6}{7}$
2. $\frac{1}{2} \div 3$	$\frac{4}{7} \div 3$	$\frac{5}{9} \div 5$	$\frac{6}{7} \div 8$
3. $\frac{1}{9} \div \frac{1}{4}$	$\frac{1}{10} \div \frac{1}{5}$	$\frac{1}{5} \div \frac{1}{10}$	$\frac{1}{3} \div \frac{1}{4}$
4. $\frac{1}{6} \div \frac{1}{9}$	$\frac{4}{5} \div \frac{3}{4}$	$\frac{7}{9} \div \frac{2}{3}$	$\frac{5}{8} \div \frac{5}{6}$
5. $2\frac{1}{3} \div 5$	$6 \div 1\frac{2}{3}$	$\frac{1}{3} \div 1\frac{1}{2}$	$3\frac{1}{3} \div 1\frac{1}{2}$

SPECTRUM MATHEMATICS,
Green Book–Second Edition

Perfect score: 20   My score: _____

PRE-TEST—Addition and Subtraction

Change each fraction or mixed numeral to a decimal.

	a	*b*	*c*
1.	$\dfrac{7}{10}=$ _____	$3\dfrac{19}{100}=$ _____	$5\dfrac{25}{1000}=$ _____

Change each of the following to a decimal as indicated.

2. Change $\frac{4}{5}$ to tenths.   Change $3\frac{8}{25}$ to hundredths.   Change $3\frac{16}{125}$ to thousandths.

Change each decimal to a fraction or mixed numeral in simplest form.

	a	*b*	*c*
3.	.8	9.33	16.125

Add or subtract.

	a	*b*	*c*	*d*
4.	.6 +.2	.7 2 +.3 5	5.3 8 2 +2.6 4 1	5.0 1 8 3.2 4 6 +5.8 1 2
5.	4.6 −3.5	5.0 5 −4.2 9	.4 5 6 −.0 1 8	1 2.0 3 8 −1.7 6 4
6.	.7 +.3 8	.2 5 6 +.8 3	1.7 +5.8 2 5	3.4 4 2.0 1 8 +.7 9
7.	.4 2 −.1	4.5 6 −1.2 4 3	5.8 −2.2 5	1 6.3 6 −1 6.0 7 5

SPECTRUM MATHEMATICS,
Green Book–Second Edition

Perfect score: 25   My score: _____

Tenths

Numerals like .4, 4.1, and 5.4 are called **decimals.**

$\frac{1}{10} = .1$ .1 is read "one tenth."

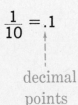

decimal points

$.4 = \frac{4}{10}$ $\frac{3}{10} = .3$

$4\frac{1}{10} = 4.1$ 4.1 is read "four and one tenth."

$5.4 = \underline{\hspace{1cm}}$ $2\frac{3}{10} = \underline{\hspace{1cm}}$

Change each fraction or mixed numeral to a decimal.

	a	*b*	*c*	*d*
1.	$\frac{6}{10} = \underline{\hspace{1cm}}$	$\frac{2}{10} = \underline{\hspace{1cm}}$	$\frac{8}{10} = \underline{\hspace{1cm}}$	$\frac{5}{10} = \underline{\hspace{1cm}}$
2.	$4\frac{7}{10} = \underline{\hspace{1cm}}$	$5\frac{9}{10} = \underline{\hspace{1cm}}$	$18\frac{2}{10} = \underline{\hspace{1cm}}$	$423\frac{6}{10} = \underline{\hspace{1cm}}$

Change each decimal to a fraction or mixed numeral.

3.	$.7 = \underline{\hspace{1cm}}$	$.3 = \underline{\hspace{1cm}}$	$.1 = \underline{\hspace{1cm}}$	$.9 = \underline{\hspace{1cm}}$
4.	$4.9 = \underline{\hspace{1cm}}$	$12.7 = \underline{\hspace{1cm}}$	$15.1 = \underline{\hspace{1cm}}$	$217.3 = \underline{\hspace{1cm}}$

Write a decimal for each of the following.

	a	*b*
5.	eight tenths _____	three and seven tenths _____
6.	four tenths _____	twenty-five and eight tenths _____
7.	five tenths _____	one hundred and six tenths _____

Write each decimal in words.

8. .9 _____

9. 3.7 _____

10. 21.2 _____

Hundredths

$\dfrac{1}{100} = .01$ .01 is read "one hundredth."

$.15 = \dfrac{15}{100}$ $\dfrac{9}{100} = .09$

$3\dfrac{12}{100} = 3.12$ 3.12 is read   "three and twelve hundredths." $2.07 =$ _____ $1\dfrac{14}{100} =$ _____

Change each fraction or mixed numeral to a decimal naming hundredths.

	a	b	c
1.	$\dfrac{8}{100} =$ _____	$\dfrac{16}{100} =$ _____	$\dfrac{5}{100} =$ _____
2.	$1\dfrac{36}{100} =$ _____	$8\dfrac{6}{100} =$ _____	$9\dfrac{12}{100} =$ _____
3.	$12\dfrac{45}{100} =$ _____	$43\dfrac{67}{100} =$ _____	$26\dfrac{4}{100} =$ _____
4.	$142\dfrac{8}{100} =$ _____	$436\dfrac{42}{100} =$ _____	$389\dfrac{89}{100} =$ _____

Change each decimal to a fraction or mixed numeral.

5.	$.17 =$ _____	$.03 =$ _____	$.41 =$ _____
6.	$5.19 =$ _____	$6.47 =$ _____	$5.01 =$ _____
7.	$21.07 =$ _____	$23.99 =$ _____	$44.89 =$ _____
8.	$142.33 =$ _____	$483.03 =$ _____	$185.63 =$ _____

Write a decimal for each of the following.

	a	b
9.	eight hundredths _____	six and twenty-three hundredths _____
10.	ninety-five hundredths _____	fourteen and sixty hundredths _____
11.	forty-eight hundredths _____	four and forty-four hundredths _____

SPECTRUM MATHEMATICS,
Green Book–Second Edition

Perfect score: 30   My score: _____

Thousandths, Ten thousandths

$\dfrac{1}{1000} = .001 \leftarrow$ one thousandth

$2\dfrac{12}{1000} = 2.012 \leftarrow$ two and twelve thousandths

$\dfrac{1}{10000} = .0001 \leftarrow$ one ten thousandth

$1\dfrac{35}{10000} = 1.0035 \leftarrow$ one and thirty-five ten thousandths

---

Write each fraction or mixed numeral as a decimal.

	a	b	c
1.	$\dfrac{8}{1000} =$ _____	$\dfrac{17}{1000} =$ _____	$\dfrac{54}{10000} =$ _____
2.	$\dfrac{125}{10000} =$ _____	$\dfrac{430}{1000} =$ _____	$\dfrac{306}{10000} =$ _____
3.	$4\dfrac{4}{1000} =$ _____	$3\dfrac{41}{10000} =$ _____	$6\dfrac{183}{1000} =$ _____
4.	$35\dfrac{78}{10000} =$ _____	$42\dfrac{19}{1000} =$ _____	$196\dfrac{6}{1000} =$ _____

Write each decimal as a fraction or as a mixed numeral.

	a	b	c
5.	.009 = _____	.0019 = _____	.0003 = _____
6.	.123 = _____	.0441 = _____	.219 = _____
7.	4.011 = _____	2.1011 = _____	6.0014 = _____
8.	36.037 = _____	3.433 = _____	100.0001 = _____

Write a decimal for each of the following.

	a	b
9.	fifty-three thousandths _____	ten and nine ten thousandths _____
10.	eleven ten thousandths _____	twelve and eighteen thousandths _____
11.	sixty-five thousandths _____	twelve and one thousandth _____

Changing Fractions and Mixed Numerals to Decimals

Change $\frac{1}{2}$ to tenths.

$$\frac{1}{2} = \frac{1}{2} \times \frac{5}{5}$$
$$= \frac{5}{10}$$
$$= .5$$

Change $\frac{1}{2}$ to hundredths.

$$\frac{1}{2} = \frac{1}{2} \times \frac{50}{50}$$
$$= \frac{50}{100}$$
$$= .50$$

Change $\frac{1}{2}$ to thousandths.

$$\frac{1}{2} = \frac{1}{2} \times \frac{500}{500}$$
$$= \frac{500}{1000}$$
$$= .500$$

Change $\frac{3}{4}$ to hundredths.

$$\frac{3}{4} = \frac{3}{4} \times \frac{25}{25}$$
$$= \frac{75}{100}$$

$$= \underline{\hspace{2cm}}$$

Change $3\frac{48}{250}$ to thousandths.

$$3\frac{48}{250} = 3 + \frac{48}{250}$$
$$= 3 + \left(\frac{48}{250} \times \frac{4}{4}\right)$$
$$= 3 + \frac{192}{1000}$$
$$= 3\frac{192}{1000}$$

$$= \underline{\hspace{2cm}}$$

Change each of the following to a decimal as indicated.

	a	b	c
1.	Change $\frac{3}{5}$ to tenths.	Change $\frac{3}{5}$ to hundredths.	Change $\frac{3}{5}$ to thousandths.
2.	Change $3\frac{1}{2}$ to tenths.	Change $\frac{7}{25}$ to hundredths.	Change $2\frac{19}{100}$ to thousandths.
3.	Change $2\frac{4}{5}$ to tenths.	Change $\frac{7}{20}$ to hundredths.	Change $\frac{7}{125}$ to thousandths.
4.	Change $2\frac{1}{5}$ to tenths.	Change $\frac{19}{50}$ to hundredths.	Change $\frac{88}{250}$ to thousandths.

Changing Decimals to Fractions or Mixed Numerals

$.7 = \frac{7}{10}$

$.19 = \frac{19}{100}$

$.6 = \frac{6}{10}$ or $\frac{3}{5}$

$.14 = \frac{14}{100}$ or $\frac{7}{50}$

$4.2 = 4\frac{2}{10}$ or $4\frac{1}{5}$

$3.01 = 3\frac{1}{100}$

$.051 = $ _____

$.114 = \frac{114}{1000}$ or _____

$5.006 = 5\frac{6}{1000}$ or _____

Change each decimal to a fraction or mixed numeral in simplest form.

	a	b	c	d
1.	.3	.1	.4	.5
2.	2.7	3.3	7.2	5.8
3.	.17	.03	.15	.80
4.	5.07	8.43	4.05	2.44
5.	.003	.017	.125	.045
6.	3.121	2.987	4.250	3.008
7.	4.35	.7	6.200	1.007
8.	2.6	3.24	.250	3.5
9.	5.125	.9	2.4	.04
10.	.01	.051	.8	2.19

SPECTRUM MATHEMATICS,
Green Book–Second Edition

Perfect score: 40   My score: _____

Fractions, Mixed Numerals, and Decimals

Change each of the following to a decimal as indicated.

	a	*b*	*c*
1.	Change $\frac{1}{5}$ to tenths.	Change $\frac{7}{20}$ to hundredths.	Change $\frac{89}{200}$ to thousandths.

2.	Change $7\frac{1}{2}$ to tenths.	Change $4\frac{29}{50}$ to hundredths.	Change $3\frac{9}{25}$ to thousandths.

Change each decimal to a fraction or mixed numeral in simplest form.

	a	*b*	*c*	*d*
3.	.9	3.6	.35	17.75
4.	.025	8.445	24.305	8.05

Complete the following so the numerals in each row name the same number.

fractions or mixed numerals	decimals		
	tenths	hundredths	thousandths
5.				.600
6.			2.70	
7.		5.4		
8.	$3\frac{1}{2}$			
9.		17.9		
10.			80.80	

SPECTRUM MATHEMATICS,
Green Book–Second Edition

Perfect score: 32   My score: _____

Addition

NAME _____

When adding decimals, line up the decimal points.
Add decimals like you add whole numbers.

```
                    1                        1
   .6       3.5 6               3.0 1 8
 +.7        .0 3               .1 4 2
 ___       +4.2 4            +1 4.0 0 9
 1.3       _____            _____
            7.8 3             1 7.1 6 9
```

↖ ─────── Place the decimal point in the answer. ─────── ↗

Add.

	a	b	c	d	e
1.	.4 +.5	.9 +.8	3.4 +9.2	1 9.3 +1 2.8	4 5.6 +6.8
2.	.4 2 +.3 5	.7 6 +.4 8	3.3 2 +4.6 2	2 4.4 5 +7 2.3 6	5 8.9 2 +3.2 9
3.	.0 1 4 +.2 3 1	.4 5 6 +.8 7 6	2.0 1 4 +2.3 2 5	3.4 5 7 +2.3 5 6	4 1.2 1 6 +2.0 0 7
4.	.5 .6 +.7	1.9 2.2 +3.4	3.4 1.7 +4.8	4 2.3 1.6 +2.9	3.4 .8 +4.2
5.	.3 3 .2 6 +.4 1	$.4 3 .5 4 +.0 7	3.3 5 1.0 8 +6.1 1	$ 2 4.2 9 1 2.2 9 +5.3 1	$ 3 4.0 5 2.0 6 +1.0 8
6.	.0 1 2 .3 0 4 +.4 0 5	.4 2 3 .0 5 6 +.2 1 7	3.0 5 6 1.4 5 2 +6.1 1 2	4.0 0 8 2.3 0 9 +.0 1 2	3 5.1 5 7 .4 4 8 +2.5 0 9

Problems

Solve each problem.

1. There was .8 inch of rain recorded on Monday, .5 inch on Tuesday, and .7 inch on Friday. How many inches of rain were recorded on those 3 days?

_____ inches were recorded.

2. In problem 1, how many inches of rain were recorded on Monday and Friday?

_____ inches were recorded.

3. A board is 4.25 meters long. Another is 3.75 meters long. When laid end to end, the boards are how long?

The boards are _____ meters long.

4. One sheet of metal is .28 centimeter thick. Another is .35 centimeter thick. What would be the combined thickness of these sheets?

The thickness would be _____ centimeter.

5. Three sheets of metal are to be placed on top of each other. Their thicknesses are .125 inch, .018 inch, and .075 inch. What would be the combined thickness of all three pieces?

The combined thickness would be _____ inch.

6. Box A weighs 1.4 pounds, box B weighs 3.2 pounds, and box C weighs 2.5 pounds. What is the combined weight of box A and box C?

The combined weight is _____ pounds.

7. In problem 6, what is the combined weight of all three boxes?

The combined weight is _____ pounds.

8. Mary Ann made three purchases at the store. The amounts were $13.75; $1.42; and $.83. What was the total amount of all three purchases?

The total amount was $_____ .

1.	
2.	
3.	
4.	
5.	
6.	
7.	
8.	

Addition

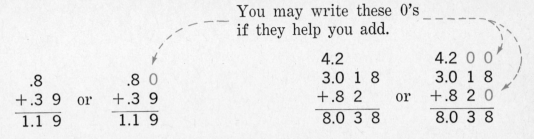

You may write these 0's
if they help you add.

	.8		.8 0
	+ .3 9	or	+ .3 9
	1.1 9		1.1 9

	4.2		4.2 0 0
	3.0 1 8		3.0 1 8
	+ .8 2	or	+ .8 2 0
	8.0 3 8		8.0 3 8

Add. If necessary, use 0's as shown in the examples.

	a	*b*	*c*	*d*	*e*
1.	.9	.8 3	.6	.7 2	.6 4 5
	+ .4 2	+ .4	+ .4 0 1	+ .4 2 3	+ .2

| 2. | 2.7 5 | 5.5 4 | 3.8 | .2 9 | 2 9.5 |
| | + 3.3 0 8 | + 7.6 | + .3 1 6 | + 8.0 4 3 | + 4.9 3 |

3.	.4 2	.3 1	.7 6	.4 3 1	.5
	.8	.2	.8 2	.2	.3 1 6
	+ .0 1 8	+ .4 5	+ .9	+ .4 5	+ .0 9 9

4.	3.1 8 2	4.7 2	7.4 2 6	.7 3 1	.3
	1.3 4	5.8	3.3 1 8	8.4 5	.3 8 4
	+ 2.6	+ 6.3 1 7	+ .2	+ 2.2 8	+ 9.4 2

Complete the following.

	a	*b*
5.	.8 + .91 = _____	.4 + .016 + .75 = _____
6.	.58 + .114 = _____	.32 + .42 + .113 = _____
7.	.9 + .301 = _____	4.8 + 3.21 + .014 = _____
8.	2.4 + .31 = _____	5.24 + .016 + 21.3 = _____

Problems

Solve each problem.

1. There was .75 inch of rain recorded at Elmhurst, .50 inch at River Forest, and .25 inch at Harvey. What amount of rain was recorded at both Elmhurst and River Forest?

The total amount was _____ inches of rain.

2. In problem **1**, how much rain was recorded at all three locations?

_____ inches were recorded.

3. An opening in an engine part is supposed to be 1.150 centimeters. The part is acceptable if the opening is as much as .075 centimeter larger than what it is supposed to be. What is the largest opening that would be acceptable?

The largest opening is _____ centimeters.

4. Assume the opening in problem **3** can only be as much as .025 centimeter larger than what it is supposed to be. What is the largest acceptable opening?

The largest opening is _____ centimeters.

5. Andy saved $23.05. Betty saved $40. Clare saved $3.50. How much have all three saved?

All three have saved a total of _____.

6. In problem **5**, how much have Andy and Clare saved?

They have saved _____.

7. In problem **5**, how much have Betty and Clare saved?
They have saved _____.

8. Marlene was asked to find the sum of 1.9; 3.52; and .075. What should her answer be?

Her answer should be _____.

1.	
2.	
3.	
4.	
5.	
6.	
7.	
8.	

Subtraction

When subtracting decimals, line up the decimal points. Subtract decimals like you subtract whole numbers.

$$
\begin{array}{r}
9.5 \\
-2.3 \\
\hline
7.2
\end{array}
\qquad
\begin{array}{r}
\overset{3\ 13}{4.\cancel{3}} \\
-1.6 \\
\hline
2.7
\end{array}
\qquad
\begin{array}{r}
\overset{0\ 14}{.\cancel{1}\ \cancel{4}} \\
-.0\ 8 \\
\hline
.0\ 6
\end{array}
\qquad
\begin{array}{r}
\overset{3\ 12\quad 4\ 13}{\cancel{4}\ 2.7\ \cancel{5}\ \cancel{3}} \\
-5.3\ 2\ 7 \\
\hline
3\ 7.4\ 2\ 6
\end{array}
$$

Place the decimal point in the answer.

Subtract.

	a	b	c	d	e
1.	.7 −.3	.9 −.2	.6 −.2	.9 −.1	.8 −.5
2.	.4 2 −.3 1	.5 6 −.2 3	.0 7 −.0 2	.8 5 −.3 7	$ .5 2 −.3 7
3.	.3 4 5 −.2 3 4	.5 4 8 −.2 5 9	.8 1 5 −.6 0 7	.8 2 8 −.3 8 9	.7 5 4 −.3 7 5
4.	4.6 −3.2	7.4 −2.8	8.6 −3.7	5.6 −.7	1 9.2 −.9
5.	4.3 6 −1.2 3	$ 6.5 5 −2.7 3	4.0 8 −.3 9	$1 5.3 2 −2.6 7	$ 4.0 9 −.3 2
6.	4.2 1 3 −2.0 0 1	3.6 2 4 −1.4 1 5	4.3 0 7 −1.4 9 5	2 6.3 4 5 −2.5 4 3	1 5.1 0 8 −3.9 1 2
7.	1 5.3 −4.9	6.2 3 −3.7 5	1 4.2 1 −7.0 8	3.0 0 2 −1.0 4 7	1 9.8 0 1 −7.4 1 3

Problems

Solve each problem.

1. Fran is to mix .8 pound of chemical A, .6 pound of chemical B, and .3 pound of chemical C. How much more of chemical A is to be used than chemical B?

_____ pound more of chemical A is to be used.

2. In problem 1, how much more of chemical A than chemical C is to be used?

_____ pound more of chemical A is to be used.

3. A spark plug has a gap of 1.12 millimeters. The gap should be .89 millimeter. How much too large is the gap?

It is _____ millimeter too large.

4. Suppose the gap in problem 3 was .65 millimeter. How much too small is the gap?

It is _____ millimeter too small.

5. Three sheets of metal were placed together. Their total thickness was 4.525 inches. Then a sheet 1.750 inches thick was removed. What was the combined thickness of the remaining sheets?

It is _____ inches thick.

6. The distance between two terminals on a television part is supposed to be 2.45 inches. The part is acceptable if the distance is .05 inches more or less than what it is supposed to be. What is the least distance that would be acceptable?

The least distance would be _____ inches.

7. One box of nails weighs 3.4 pounds and another box weighs 5.2 pounds. How much more does the heavier box weigh?

The heavier box weighs _____ pounds more.

1.

2.

3.

4.

5.

6.

7.

SPECTRUM MATHEMATICS,
Green Book–Second Edition

Perfect score: 7   My score: _____

Subtraction

$$\begin{array}{r} \overset{5\ 14}{6.4}\ 3\ 2 \\ -1.7 \\ \hline 4.7\ 3\ 2 \end{array} \quad \text{or} \quad \begin{array}{r} \overset{5\ 14}{6.4}\ 3\ 2 \\ -1.7\ 0\ 0 \\ \hline 4.7\ 3\ 2 \end{array}$$ ←— Write these 0's if they help you.

$$\begin{array}{r} 6.4 \\ -1.2\ 3 \end{array} \rightarrow \begin{array}{r} \overset{3\ 10}{6.4}\ \cancel{0} \\ -1.2\ 3 \\ \hline 5.1\ 7 \end{array}$$ ←— Write this 0 to help you subtract.

Subtract.

	a	b	c	d	e
1.	.7 2 − .2	3.5 6 −1.4	5.3 8 −2.7	4.3 1 6 −1.1	2.1 4 6 −1.5
2.	.5 2 3 −.4 1	.6 8 3 −.3 9	5.4 2 1 − .5 6	3.0 1 8 − .2 7	4.0 1 2 −3.0 3
3.	.8 −.3 5	.5 −.2 6	6.3 −1.1 2	7.4 −2.7 5	1 4.3 −6.7 2
4.	.9 −.3 0 9	.3 −.1 7 5	4.4 −2.3 5 6	6.3 −3.4 3 2	1 8.2 −7.5 1 4
5.	.7 5 −.3 1 4	.3 6 −.2 7 5	5.7 2 −1.3 1 2	4.3 8 −.5 9 2	1 6.9 2 −6.3 8 4
6.	3 4.2 6 5 −2.1 8	4 2.1 6 −3.2 3 5	4 2.2 −3.1 6 4	2 6.3 − 2.4 5	3.1 0 6 −2.0 3
7.	4 3.7 −6.1 8	3 9 4.6 −7 5.8 1	5.2 1 6 −4.1 9	8 2.4 5 −3.7 8 3	9 2.4 0 5 −3.0 0 8

SPECTRUM MATHEMATICS,
 Green Book–Second Edition

Perfect score: 35   My score: _____

Problems

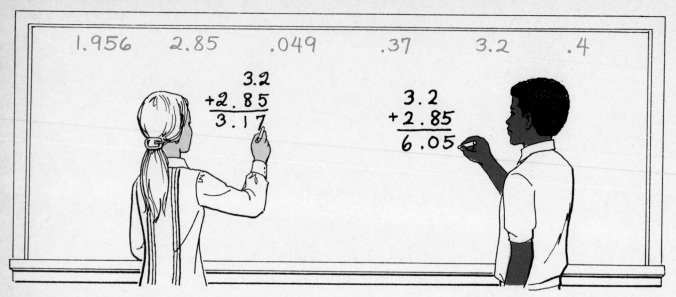

Solve each problem.

1. Mr. Prinkle told the pupils to find the sum of the two greatest numbers named in color on the board. Kay and Ralph did their work at the board. Who worked the problem correctly? What is the correct answer?

2. Next the pupils were to find the difference between the two greatest numbers named. What should the answer be?

3. Next they were to find the sum of the three greatest numbers named. What should the answer be?

4. Then they were to find the sum of the three least numbers named. What should the answer be?

5. Finally the pupils were to find the difference between the sum of the three greatest numbers and the sum of the three least numbers. What should the answer be?

1.	**2.**
3.	**4.**
5.	

SPECTRUM MATHEMATICS,
Green Book–Second Edition

Perfect score: 6   My score: _____

TEST—Addition and Subtraction

Change each fraction or mixed numeral to a decimal.

	a	*b*	*c*
1.	$\dfrac{175}{1000} =$ _____	$9\dfrac{4}{10} =$ _____	$3\dfrac{8}{100} =$ _____

Change each of the following to a decimal as indicated.

2.   Change $\dfrac{9}{10}$ to hundredths.   Change $3\dfrac{1}{5}$ to tenths.   Change $5\dfrac{75}{250}$ to thousandths.

Change each decimal to a fraction or mixed numeral in simplest form.

	a	*b*	*c*
3.	.075	8.6	16.49

Add or subtract.

	a	*b*	*c*	*d*
4.	.9 +.4	.5 2 +.4 3	6.5 3 4 +7.8 2 7	9.3 0 8 2 1.2 9 5 +.0 4 3
5.	3.3 −1.6	8.2 4 −3.7 3	.4 4 2 −.3 7 5	1 8.0 4 2 −1 2.3 4 5
6.	.4 2 +.9	.3 5 +.0 6 5	3.6 +1 4.6 7 3	9.2 4.3 7 5 +4 3.7 8
7.	.5 4 6 −.3 8	3.8 −1.2 1	7.2 2 −4.4 3 6	8.4 −3.5 7 5

PRE-TEST—Multiplication

Multiply.

	a	*b*	*c*	*d*	*e*
1.	.7 ×5	.4 ×2	4 ×.9	4 ×.3	5 ×.6
2.	.0 7 ×6	.0 2 ×3	8 ×.0 4	8 ×.0 9	5 ×.0 8
3.	.0 0 3 ×4	.0 0 1 ×8	2 ×.0 0 3	4 ×.0 0 1	6 ×.0 0 2
4.	.7 ×.3	.2 ×.4	.4 ×.6	.9 ×.6	.8 ×.5
5.	.0 6 ×.8	.0 1 ×.5	.2 ×.0 3	.0 6 ×.0 7	.0 2 ×.0 2
6.	.4 ×1 0	.0 0 8 ×1 0 0	6.7 2 ×1 0	.2 3 4 ×1 0 0 0	5.6 8 ×1 0 0 0
7.	1 6 ×.3	.4 7 ×.5	3.4 ×.0 8	5.0 1 ×.2 5	.0 7 8 ×7.5

SPECTRUM MATHEMATICS,
Green Book–Second Edition

Perfect score: 35   My score: _____

Multiplication

number of digits to the right of the
decimal point -

4	.4	1	.04	2	.04	2	.04	2
×3	×3	+0	×3	+0	×.3	+1	×.03	+2
12	1.2	1	.12	2	.012	3	.0012	4

Write in as many 0's as needed to
place the decimal point correctly.

Multiply.

	a	b	c	d	e
1.	2 ×3	.2 ×3	.0 2 ×3	.0 0 2 ×3	2 ×.3
2.	8 ×6	.8 ×6	.0 8 ×6	.0 0 8 ×6	.0 6 ×8
3.	5 ×3	.5 ×3	.0 5 ×3	.0 0 5 ×3	.0 0 3 ×5
4.	3 ×4	.3 ×.4	.0 3 ×.4	.0 4 ×.3	.0 3 ×.0 4
5.	6 ×7	.6 ×.7	.0 6 ×.7	.0 7 ×.6	.0 6 ×.0 7
6.	9 ×8	.9 ×.8	.0 9 ×.8	.0 8 ×.9	.0 9 ×.0 8

Multiplication

number of digits to the right of the
decimal point

24	2.4	1	.24	2	.24	2	.24	2
×36	×36	+0	×36	+0	×3.6	+1	×.36	+2
864	86.4	1	8.64	2	.864	3	.0864	4

Use the completed multiplication to find each product.

		a	b	c	d
1.	32 ×14 448	3.2 ×14	.32 ×14	.32 ×1.4	.32 ×.14
2.	27 ×48 1296	2.7 ×48	.27 ×48	.27 ×4.8	.27 ×.48
3.	26 ×34 884	.26 ×34	.26 ×3.4	.26 ×.34	2.6 ×34
4.	74 ×26 1924	.74 ×2.6	7.4 ×26	.74 ×26	.74 ×.26
5.	25 ×3 75	25 ×.3	2.5 ×.03	25 ×.03	.25 ×.03
6.	12 ×4 48	1.2 ×.4	.12 ×4	.12 ×.4	.12 ×.04
7.	73 ×3 219	73 ×.03	.73 ×.03	7.3 ×.3	.73 ×.3

Multiplication

6	.6	.6	.06	.06	.06	.006
×3	×3	×.3	×3	×.3	×.03	×.3
18	1.8	.18	.18	.018	.0018	.0018

Multiply.

	a	b	c	d	e
1.	.7 ×5	3 ×.2	.8 ×9	7 ×.3	.2 ×4
2.	.8 ×.6	.1 ×.6	.3 ×.7	.2 ×.4	.7 ×.6
3.	.0 8 ×4	.0 2 ×3	7 ×.0 8	.0 9 ×6	5 ×.0 3
4.	.0 5 ×.9	.7 ×.0 5	.0 8 ×.8	.2 ×.0 3	.0 3 ×.5
5.	.0 3 ×.0 8	.0 4 ×.0 6	.0 9 ×.0 1	.0 7 ×.0 8	.0 3 ×.0 2
6.	.0 0 7 ×9	6 ×.0 0 8	.0 0 4 ×6	.0 0 8 ×4	5 ×.0 0 7
7.	.0 0 5 ×.9	.0 0 9 ×.9	.3 ×.0 0 4	.0 0 3 ×.3	.5 ×.0 0 5

SPECTRUM MATHEMATICS,
Green Book–Second Edition

Perfect score: 35   My score: _____

Multiplication

2.51	2.51	2.51
×10	×100	×1000
25.10	251.00	2510.00
or	or	or
25.1	251	2510

Shortcut

2.51 × 10 = 2 5.1

2.51 × 100 = 2 51

2.51 × 1000 = 2 510

.085	.085	.085
×10	×100	×1000
.850	8.500	85.000
or	or	or
.85	8.5	85

.085 × 10 = 0.85

.085 × 100 = 08.5

.085 × 1000 = 085

Multiply.

	a	b	c	d	e
1.	5.6 4 2 ×1 0	5.6 4 2 ×1 0 0	5.6 4 2 ×1 0 0 0	5 6.4 2 ×1 0 0	.5 6 4 2 ×1 0
2.	.1 0 6 4 ×1 0	.1 0 6 4 ×1 0 0	.1 0 6 4 ×1 0 0 0	.0 1 0 6 ×1 0	1.0 6 4 ×1 0 0 0
3.	.2 3 ×1 0	.2 3 ×1 0 0	.2 3 ×1 0 0 0	.0 2 3 ×1 0	.0 0 2 3 ×1 0 0
4.	.0 0 8 ×1 0	.0 0 8 ×1 0 0	.0 0 8 ×1 0 0 0	.0 8 ×1 0 0	.0 8 ×1 0 0 0
5.	1.5 ×1 0	1.5 ×1 0 0	1.5 ×1 0 0 0	1 5 ×1 0 0	.1 5 ×1 0

Multiplication

	Multiply as whole numbers.		Place the decimal point in the product.

$$
\begin{array}{r} .356 \\ \times 4.2 \\ \hline \end{array}
\quad \longrightarrow \quad
\begin{array}{r} .356 \\ \times 4.2 \\ \hline 712 \\ 1424 \\ \hline 14952 \end{array}
\quad \longrightarrow \quad
\begin{array}{r} .356 \\ \times 4.2 \\ \hline 712 \\ 1424 \\ \hline 1.4952 \end{array}
$$

Multiply.

1.
$$\begin{array}{r} 43 \\ \times .08 \\ \hline \end{array} \qquad \begin{array}{r} 5.4 \\ \times .04 \\ \hline \end{array} \qquad \begin{array}{r} .076 \\ \times .7 \\ \hline \end{array} \qquad \begin{array}{r} .18 \\ \times .09 \\ \hline \end{array} \qquad \begin{array}{r} .092 \\ \times 8 \\ \hline \end{array}$$

2.
$$\begin{array}{r} .137 \\ \times .3 \\ \hline \end{array} \qquad \begin{array}{r} 4.82 \\ \times 8 \\ \hline \end{array} \qquad \begin{array}{r} 907 \\ \times .4 \\ \hline \end{array} \qquad \begin{array}{r} 6.53 \\ \times .7 \\ \hline \end{array} \qquad \begin{array}{r} .416 \\ \times 6 \\ \hline \end{array}$$

3.
$$\begin{array}{r} 32.1 \\ \times .5 \\ \hline \end{array} \qquad \begin{array}{r} 5.06 \\ \times 4 \\ \hline \end{array} \qquad \begin{array}{r} .0709 \\ \times 4 \\ \hline \end{array} \qquad \begin{array}{r} .421 \\ \times .2 \\ \hline \end{array} \qquad \begin{array}{r} .0503 \\ \times 9 \\ \hline \end{array}$$

4.
$$\begin{array}{r} .27 \\ \times 4.2 \\ \hline \end{array} \qquad \begin{array}{r} 5.8 \\ \times .16 \\ \hline \end{array} \qquad \begin{array}{r} .03 \\ \times 2.5 \\ \hline \end{array} \qquad \begin{array}{r} .42 \\ \times .53 \\ \hline \end{array} \qquad \begin{array}{r} 7.6 \\ \times 7.6 \\ \hline \end{array}$$

5.
$$\begin{array}{r} .187 \\ \times 3.5 \\ \hline \end{array} \qquad \begin{array}{r} .084 \\ \times 42 \\ \hline \end{array} \qquad \begin{array}{r} 16.1 \\ \times 5.3 \\ \hline \end{array} \qquad \begin{array}{r} .072 \\ \times 6.2 \\ \hline \end{array} \qquad \begin{array}{r} 5.21 \\ \times .75 \\ \hline \end{array}$$

6.
$$\begin{array}{r} 42.16 \\ \times 1.8 \\ \hline \end{array} \qquad \begin{array}{r} .4218 \\ \times 22 \\ \hline \end{array} \qquad \begin{array}{r} 306.4 \\ \times .24 \\ \hline \end{array} \qquad \begin{array}{r} .0314 \\ \times 26 \\ \hline \end{array} \qquad \begin{array}{r} .0144 \\ \times 37 \\ \hline \end{array}$$

SPECTRUM MATHEMATICS,
Green Book–Second Edition

Perfect score: 30   My score: _____

Problems

Solve each problem.

1. A box of seeds weighs .9 pound. How many pounds would 6 boxes weigh?

They would weigh _____ pounds.

2. A machinist has 4 sheets of metal, each .042 inch thick. These are placed one on top of the other. What is the total thickness of the sheets?

It will be _____ inch thick.

3. Each needle weighs .03 gram. How many grams would 100 needles weigh?

They would weigh _____ grams.

4. A log weighs 42.1 kilograms. How much would .5 of the log weigh?

It would weigh _____ kilograms.

5. The thickness of a sheet of plastic is .024 inch. What would be the combined thickness of 6 sheets of plastic?

The combined thickness would be _____ inch.

6. In problem 5, what would be the combined thickness of 8 sheets of plastic?

The combined thickness would be _____ inch.

7. Mrs. Tomasello has 92 sheets of foil. Each sheet is .0413 inch thick. What is the combined thickness of the sheets?

The thickness would be _____ inches.

8. Mr. McClean's car averages 5.7 kilometers per liter of gasoline. How many kilometers would he be able to travel with 84 liters of gasoline?

He could travel _____ kilometers.

9. Suppose the car in problem 8 averages 4.9 kilometers per liter. How far could the car go on 84 liters of gasoline?

It could go _____ kilometers.

1.	2.
3.	4.
5.	6.
7.	8.
9.	

SPECTRUM MATHEMATICS,
Green Book–Second Edition

Perfect score: 9   My score: _____

Multiplication

NAME _____

Multiply.

	a	b	c	d
1.	.6 ×.4	.0 8 × 9	.0 7 ×.0 7	.0 0 5 × 8
2.	4.5 ×.2 7	.3 8 ×.3 2	2.6 ×.0 4 3	7.5 ×2.5
3.	.1 4 9 ×5 3	4 7.6 ×.0 4 2	3.0 8 ×5.3	.7 2 9 ×6.1
4.	3 5.4 6 ×.2 7	3 1 8.2 ×.3 6	9.8 0 4 ×2 6	8 0 0.6 ×.0 4 3
5.	7.2 1 ×5.3 4	4 0.7 ×4.3 1	3 1 2 ×.0 6 2 4	.5 9 8 ×7 5.3

SPECTRUM MATHEMATICS,
Green Book–Second Edition

Perfect score: 20   My score: _____

89

Problems

Solve each problem.

1. Each box of bolts weighs 1.7 pounds. There are 24 boxes in a carton. How many pounds would a carton of bolts weigh?

A carton would weigh _____ pounds.

2. A sheet of paper is .012 centimeter thick. How many centimeters thick would a stack of paper be if it contained 28 sheets of paper?

The stack would be _____ centimeter thick.

3. Each sheet of metal is .024 centimeter thick. There are 67 sheets of metal in a stack. How high is the stack?

The stack is _____ centimeters high.

4. Miss Wilson wrote $4.2 \times 264.3 = \underline{\ ?\ }$ and $4.2 \times 26.43 = \underline{\ ?\ }$ on the board. She told the pupils to solve the problems and write the answer that names the greatest product. What is the correct answer?

The correct answer is _____.

5. Miss Wilson wrote $6.41 \times .035 = \underline{\ ?\ }$ and $64.1 \times .35 = \underline{\ ?\ }$ on the board. She told the pupils to solve the problems and write the answer that names the least product. What is the correct answer?

The correct answer is _____.

6. Each container filled with chemical X weighs 32.7 pounds. How many pounds would 100 containers weigh?

They would weigh _____ pounds.

7. Mr. Wilcox wrote 30.8; 308; and 3.08 on the board. He told the pupils to find the product of the two greatest numbers named. What should the answer be?

The answer should be _____.

8. Suppose in problem **7** the pupils had been asked to find the product of the two least numbers named. What should the answer be?

The answer should be _____.

1.	2.
3.	4.
5.	6.
7.	8.

SPECTRUM MATHEMATICS,
Green Book–Second Edition

Perfect score: 8   My score: _____

TEST—Multiplication

Multiply.

	a	b	c	d	e
1.	.6 ×.8	.18 ×7	.308 ×.9	.42 ×5.3	1.73 ×2.8
2.	9 ×.6	2.4 ×.3	42.6 ×.7	.64 ×.75	146 ×.52
3.	.05 ×.3	.64 ×.9	3.15 ×.9	5.8 ×6.1	35.6 ×.42
4.	4 ×.02	5.3 ×.04	6.02 ×.04	7.81 ×15.2	.1628 ×100
5.	.9 ×.006	.67 ×.02	532 ×.07	3.86 ×4.04	418 ×.632

SPECTRUM MATHEMATICS,
Green Book–Second Edition

Perfect score: 25   My score: _____

PRE-TEST—Division

Divide.

	a	b	c	d

1. $2\overline{)14.6}$ $7\overline{)1.89}$ $9\overline{).405}$ $6\overline{).0114}$

2. $.3\overline{)6}$ $.5\overline{)75}$ $.02\overline{)42}$ $.004\overline{)16}$

3. $.6\overline{).72}$ $.3\overline{)6.3}$ $.04\overline{).096}$ $.003\overline{).015}$

4. $.04\overline{)3.2}$ $.08\overline{)4.8}$ $.002\overline{)7.26}$ $.003\overline{)1.8}$

5. $.18\overline{)27}$ $1.7\overline{).238}$ $4.6\overline{)2.116}$ $.38\overline{).3496}$

SPECTRUM MATHEMATICS,
Green Book–Second Edition

Perfect score: 20   My score: _____

Division

Place a decimal point in the quotient directly above the decimal point in the dividend. Then divide as if both numbers were whole numbers.

```
    17           1.7          .17         .017
6 | 102       6 | 10.2     6 | 1.02     6 | .102
    60           60           60           60
    ──           ──           ──           ──
    42           42           42           42
    42           42           42           42
    ──           ──           ──           ──
     0            0            0            0
```

Divide.

	a	b	c	d	e

1. 4)292   4)29.2   4)2.92   4).292   4).0292

2. 3)5.61   8).0216   7).231   4)4.64   6)25.2

3. 7)24.5   8).336   6).0162   4)24.4   3)1.68

Perfect score: 15   My score: _____

Problems

Solve each problem.

1. A wire .8 inch long is to be cut into 4 pieces each the same length. How long will each piece be?

Each piece will be _____ inch long.

2. The same amount of flour was used in each of 3 batches of bread dough. A total of 6.9 kilograms was used. How much flour was in each batch?

_____ kilograms of flour was in each batch.

3. The combined thickness of 5 sheets of metal is .015 inch. Each sheet has the same thickness. How thick is each sheet?

Each sheet is _____ inch thick.

4. Each of 7 bolts has the same weight. Their total weight is .42 pound. How much does each bolt weigh?

Each bolt weighs _____ pound.

5. Mr. Rinkles wrote .08; 8; and .008 on the board. He told the pupils to divide the least number named by the greatest number named. What is the answer?

The answer is _____.

6. Mr. Rinkles wrote 4; 72.4; and 7.24 on the board. He told the pupils to divide the greatest number named by the least number named. What is the correct answer?

The correct answer is _____.

7. A sheet of film is .072 centimeter thick. It is 6 times thicker than needed. What thickness is needed?

_____ centimeter is needed.

8. A sheet of film is .0672 inch thick. It is 8 times thicker than needed. What thickness is needed?

_____ inch is needed.

1.	2.
3.	4.
5.	6.
7.	8.

SPECTRUM MATHEMATICS,
Green Book–Second Edition

Perfect score: 8   My score: _____

Division

Multiply the divisor and the dividend by 10, by 100, or by 1000 so the new divisor is a whole number.

$.8\overline{)32}$ ⟶ $.8\overline{)32.0}$ ⟶ $\begin{array}{r} 40 \\ 8\overline{)320} \\ \underline{320} \\ 0 \end{array}$ Multiply by 10.

$.004\overline{)26}$ ⟶ $.004\overline{)26.000}$ ⟶ $\begin{array}{r} 6500 \\ 4\overline{)26000} \\ \underline{24000} \\ 2000 \\ \underline{2000} \\ 0 \end{array}$ Multiply by 1000.

$.05\overline{)45}$ ⟶ $.05\overline{)45.00}$ ⟶ $\begin{array}{r} 900 \\ 5\overline{)4500} \\ \underline{4500} \\ 0 \end{array}$ Multiply by 100.

Divide.

	a	b	c	d
1.	$.4\overline{)72}$	$.3\overline{)81}$	$.7\overline{)357}$	$.3\overline{)111}$
2.	$.03\overline{)54}$	$.04\overline{)96}$	$.05\overline{)85}$	$.08\overline{)296}$
3.	$.002\overline{)6}$	$.004\overline{)12}$	$.006\overline{)24}$	$.005\overline{)155}$

Problems

Solve each problem.

1. Dick put 72 kilograms of honey into jars. He put .4 kilogram into each jar. How many jars did he use?

He used _____ jars.

2. A machine uses .3 gallon of fuel each hour. How many hours could the machine operate with 39 gallons of fuel?

The machine could operate _____ hours.

3. Each metal bar weighs .04 kilogram. How many metal bars would weigh 520 kilograms?

_____ metal bars would weigh 520 kilograms.

4. A machine uses .3 gallon of fuel each hour. At that rate, how many hours could the machine operate by using 195 gallons of fuel?

The machine could operate _____ hours.

5. Eight-tenths gram of a chemical is put into each jar. How many jars can be filled with 192 grams of the chemical?

_____ jars can be filled.

6. Each sheet of foil is .004 inch thick. How many sheets would be in a stack of foil that is 5 inches high?

There would be _____ sheets.

7. Miss Pruit wrote .6; .006; 6; and .06 on the board. She told the pupils to divide the greatest number named by the least number named. What is the correct answer?

The correct answer is _____.

8. Each class period lasts .5 hour. How many class periods could there be in 6 hours?

There could be _____ periods.

1.	2.
3.	4.
5.	6.
7.	8.

SPECTRUM MATHEMATICS,
Green Book–Second Edition

Perfect score: 8   My score: _____

Division

$$.5\overline{)11.5} \longrightarrow .5\overline{)11.5} \longrightarrow 5\overline{)115}$$

Multiply
by 10.

$$\begin{array}{r} 23 \\ 5\overline{)115} \\ \underline{100} \\ 15 \\ \underline{15} \\ 0 \end{array}$$

$$.06\overline{).426} \longrightarrow .06\overline{).426} \longrightarrow 6\overline{)42.6}$$

Multiply
by 100.

$$\begin{array}{r} 7.1 \\ 6\overline{)42.6} \\ \underline{420} \\ 6 \\ \underline{6} \\ 0 \end{array}$$

$$.003\overline{)2.1} \longrightarrow .003\overline{)2.100} \longrightarrow 3\overline{)2100}$$

Multiply
by 1000.

$$\begin{array}{r} 700 \\ 3\overline{)2100} \\ \underline{2100} \\ 0 \end{array}$$

Divide.

	a	b	c	d
1.	$.4\overline{)7.2}$	$.3\overline{).81}$	$.8\overline{).392}$	$.6\overline{)55.2}$
2.	$.06\overline{).84}$	$.04\overline{).068}$	$.08\overline{).224}$	$.07\overline{)2.52}$
3.	$.002\overline{).008}$	$.007\overline{).0042}$	$.008\overline{).144}$	$.009\overline{).0333}$
4.	$.004\overline{).096}$	$.09\overline{)6.3}$	$.006\overline{).009}$	$.7\overline{)8.4}$

Division

Divide.

	a	b	c	d

1. $.03\overline{)1.8}$ $.06\overline{)28.8}$ $.04\overline{)9.2}$ $.05\overline{)1.5}$

2. $.003\overline{)2.4}$ $.009\overline{).45}$ $.008\overline{)2.16}$ $.005\overline{)2.5}$

3. $.02\overline{)7.4}$ $.006\overline{)10.2}$ $.08\overline{)27.2}$ $.008\overline{)9.6}$

4. $.05\overline{)3.25}$ $.06\overline{)4.2}$ $.002\overline{).4}$ $.004\overline{).56}$

5. $.3\overline{)75}$ $.007\overline{)56.7}$ $.09\overline{)74.7}$ $.005\overline{)48}$

Division

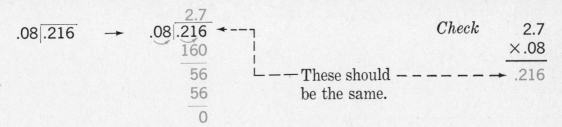

$$.08\overline{).216} \rightarrow .08\overline{).216}$$

$$\begin{array}{r} 2.7 \\ .08\overline{).216} \\ \underline{160} \\ 56 \\ \underline{56} \\ 0 \end{array}$$

These should be the same.

Check
$$\begin{array}{r} 2.7 \\ \times .08 \\ \hline .216 \end{array}$$

Divide. Check each answer.

       a   *b*   *c*

1. $3\overline{)1.44}$ $6\overline{)17.4}$ $5\overline{).085}$

2. $.3\overline{)45}$ $.003\overline{)12}$ $.07\overline{)14}$

3. $.7\overline{).98}$ $.006\overline{)31.8}$ $.08\overline{).632}$

4. $.03\overline{)4.2}$ $.004\overline{)7.2}$ $.006\overline{)1.68}$

5. $.08\overline{)9.6}$ $.003\overline{)84}$ $6\overline{)9.6}$

Problems

Solve each problem. Check each answer.

1. Three-tenths pound of chemical is put into each container. How many containers can be filled with 5.4 pounds of chemical?

_____ containers can be filled.

2. Seventy-five hundredths pound of product Y is to be put into containers that hold .5 pound each. How many full containers will there be? What part of the next container will be filled?

There will be _____ full container.

_____ of the next container will be filled.

3. There are 10.2 pounds of ball bearings in a box. Each bearing weighs .006 pound. How many bearings are in the box?

There are _____ bearings in the box.

4. A machine processes 1.95 pounds of chemical every 3 hours. At that rate, how many pounds of chemical are processed in 1 hour?

_____ pounds are processed.

5. Each sheet of metal is .005 inch thick. How many sheets of metal would there be in a stack that is 4.2 inches high?

There would be _____ sheets.

6. A wire that is .6 meter long is cut into pieces of the same length. Each piece is .06 meter long. How many pieces of wire are there?

There are _____ pieces.

7. Suppose in problem 6 each piece of wire is .006 meter long. How many pieces are there?

There are _____ pieces.

1.	2.
3.	4.
5.	6.
7.	

Division

$$.25\overline{)1} \longrightarrow .25\overline{)100} \longrightarrow 25\overline{)100}$$

```
        4
  25)100
      100
        0
```

$$2.7\overline{)3.78} \longrightarrow 2.7\overline{)3.78} \longrightarrow 27\overline{)37.8}$$

```
       1.4
  27)37.8
      270
      108
      108
        0
```

Divide.

	a	b	c	d

1. $.20\overline{)1}$ $.15\overline{)9}$ $.028\overline{)1\ 4}$ $.012\overline{)6}$

2. $1.2\overline{)3.9\ 6}$ $.42\overline{).7\ 5\ 6}$ $.18\overline{).8\ 2\ 8}$ $2.5\overline{).6\ 2\ 5}$

3. $.67\overline{).3\ 8\ 8\ 6}$ $.45\overline{)1.2\ 1\ 5}$ $7.3\overline{)3\ 0.6\ 6}$ $4.3\overline{).1\ 3\ 7\ 6}$

4. $.025\overline{)7\ 5}$ $.36\overline{)1.5\ 1\ 2}$ $5.4\overline{).3\ 9\ 4\ 2}$ $.53\overline{).6\ 3\ 6}$

Problems

Solve each problem.

1. A carton of items weighs 28.8 pounds. Each item weighs 3.6 pounds. How many items are in the carton?

_____ items are in the carton.

2. There is .444 pound of chemical to be put into tubes. Each tube holds .12 pound. How many tubes will be filled? How much of another tube is filled?

_____ tubes will be filled.

_____ of the next tube will be filled.

3. A stack of cardboard is 52 inches high. Each piece is .65 inch thick. How many pieces of cardboard are in the stack?

_____ pieces are in the stack.

4. How many pieces each .25 inch long can be cut from a wire that is 2 inches long?

_____ pieces can be cut from the wire.

5. How many pieces each .5 inch long can be cut from the wire described in problem 4?

_____ pieces can be cut from the wire.

6. Each bag of flour weighs 2.2 pounds. How many such bags can be filled by using 11 pounds of flour?

_____ bags can be filled.

7. Consider the numbers named by .016; 1.6; and .16. What is the quotient if you divide the greatest number by the least number?

The quotient is _____.

8. Suppose in problem 7 you divide the least number by the greatest number. What is the quotient?

The quotient is _____.

1.	2.
3.	4.
5.	6.
7.	8.

SPECTRUM MATHEMATICS,
Green Book–Second Edition

Perfect score: 9   My score: _____

Division

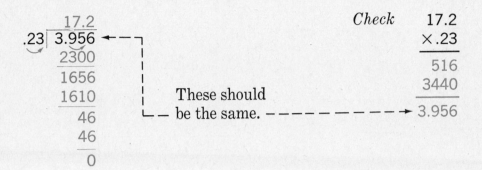

Divide. Check each answer.

	a	b	c
1.	.73$\overline{)5.986}$	5.6$\overline{).672}$	.15$\overline{)75}$
2.	2.1$\overline{)6.93}$	.15$\overline{)18}$	.083$\overline{)6.308}$
3.	.37$\overline{).1739}$	1.6$\overline{)4.48}$	.53$\overline{)4.876}$

Problems

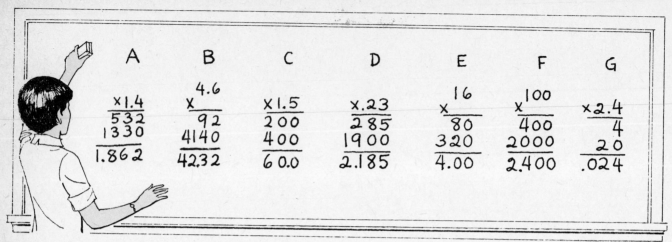

Solve each problem.

1. Before class Yoshiko worked some multiplication problems on the board. Then she erased a numeral in each problem. When the pupils came into the classroom, she asked them to discover what numerals had been erased. What numeral was erased in problem A?

_____ was erased in problem A.

2. What numeral was erased in problem B?

_____ was erased in problem B.

3. What numeral was erased in problem C?

_____ was erased in problem C.

4. What numeral was erased in problem D?

_____ was erased in problem D.

5. What numeral was erased in problem E?

_____ was erased in problem E.

6. What numeral was erased in problem F?

_____ was erased in problem F.

7. What numeral was erased in problem G?

_____ was erased in problem G?

1.	
2.	3.
4.	5.
6.	7.

TEST—Division

Divide.

	a	*b*	*c*	*d*

1. $8\overline{).184}$ $3\overline{).42}$ $4\overline{)14.8}$ $6\overline{).0306}$

2. $.05\overline{)55}$ $.003\overline{)36}$ $.7\overline{)42}$ $.04\overline{)84}$

3. $.4\overline{)9.2}$ $.6\overline{).84}$ $.03\overline{).072}$ $.004\overline{).028}$

4. $.006\overline{)5.4}$ $.07\overline{)4.9}$ $.007\overline{).63}$ $.004\overline{)41.2}$

5. $.36\overline{)9}$ $3.8\overline{)5.32}$ $.42\overline{)1.092}$ $4.5\overline{).3285}$

SPECTRUM MATHEMATICS,
Green Book–Second Edition

Perfect score: 20   My score: _____

PRE-TEST—Metric Measurement

a   b

1. 7 meters = _____ millimeters   85 millimeters = _____ meter

2. 1.9 meters = _____ centimeters   4.5 centimeters = _____ meter

3. 6 kilometers = _____ meters   7 meters = _____ kilometer

4. 5 liters = _____ milliliters   4000 milliliters = _____ liters

5. 3.5 kiloliters = _____ liters   6.5 liters = _____ kiloliter

6. 8.2 kilograms = _____ grams   255 grams = _____ kilogram

Find the area of each rectangle.

a   b

7.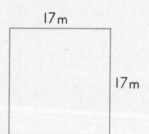

_____ square meters   _____ square centimeters

Find the volume of each rectangular solid.

a   b

8.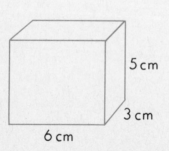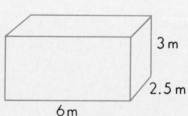

_____ cubic centimeters   _____ cubic meters

SPECTRUM MATHEMATICS,
Green Book–Second Edition

Perfect score: 16   My score: _____

Length

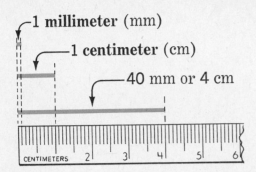

10 mm = 1 cm	1 mm = .1 cm
1000 mm = 1 m	1 mm = .001 m
100 cm = 1 m	1 cm = .01 m
1000 m = 1 km	1 m = .001 km

100 cm or 1 meter (m)

A distance of 1000 meters is **1 kilometer** (km).

Measure the following to the nearest meter.

a   *b*

1. height of classroom door _____ m   width of room _____ m

2. width of classroom door _____ m   length of room _____ m

3. One kilometer is about the length of 5 blocks.
About how many kilometers do you live from school? _____ km

Find the length of each line segment to the nearest centimeter.

4. _____ cm

5. _____ cm

Find the length of each line segment to the nearest millimeter.

6. _____ mm

7. _____ mm

Draw a line segment for each measurement.

8. 6 cm

9. 8 cm

10. 35 mm

Units of Length

160 m = _____?_____ km   7.2 cm = _____?_____ mm

1 m = .001 km   1 cm = 10 mm
(160 × 1) m = (160 × .001) km   (7.2 × 1) cm = (7.2 × 10) mm

160 m = _____.16_____ km   7.2 cm = _____72_____ mm

Find the length of each line segment to the nearest millimeter.
Then give the length in centimeters and in meters.

	a	b	c

1. _____ mm _____ cm _____ m

2. _____ mm _____ cm _____ m

3. _____ mm _____ cm _____ m

4. _____ mm _____ cm _____ m

5. _____ mm _____ cm _____ m

Complete the following.

a	b	c

6. 54 mm = _____ cm   8 m = _____ mm   234 m = _____ km

7. 1.6 m = _____ cm   .9 cm = _____ mm   58 mm = _____ cm

8. 612 mm = _____ m   4 km = _____ m   13 mm = _____ cm

9. .02 m = _____ mm   .75 km = _____ m   34.5 m = _____ km

10. 707 cm = _____ m   .005 m = _____ cm   465 mm = _____ cm

SPECTRUM MATHEMATICS,
Green Book–Second Edition

Perfect score: 30   My score: _____

Area

To find the *area measure* (A) of a rectangle, multiply the measure of its *length* (l) by the measure of its *width* (w).

6m
4.2 m [rectangle]

$A = l \times w$
$= 6 \times 4.2$
$= 25.2$

The area is __25.2__ square meters.

15 mm
15mm [square]

$A = l \times w$
$= 15 \times 15$
$= 225$

The area is _____ square millimeters.

Measure the sides as indicated. Then find the area of each rectangle.

a

b

1.

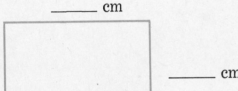

_____ cm

_____ cm

_____ square centimeters

_____ cm

_____ cm

_____ square centimeters

2.

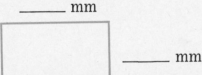

_____ mm

_____ mm

_____ square millimeters

_____ mm

_____ mm

_____ square millimeters

Find the area of each rectangle described below.

	length	width	area
3.	5.8 km	3 km	_____ square kilometers
4.	4.5 m	4.5 m	_____ square meters
5.	32.4 m	16 m	_____ square meters

Problems

Solve each problem.

1. A rectangular piece of plywood is 150 centimeters long. It is 75 centimeters wide. Find the area of the piece of plywood.

The area is _____ square centimeters.

2. A rectangular piece of carpet is 6 meters long and 4.5 meters wide. How many square meters of carpet is that?

That is _____ square meters of carpet.

3. A rectangular floor is 8.5 meters long and 6.5 meters wide. How many square meters of floor are there?

There are _____ square meters of floor.

4. A playground is shaped like a rectangle. Its length is 140 meters. Its width is 60 meters. Find the area of the playground.

The area is _____ square meters.

5. A rectangular poster is 35 centimeters wide and 52 centimeters long. Find the area of the poster.

The area is _____ square centimeters.

6. A rectangular postcard is 8.5 centimeters wide and 14 centimeters long. Find the area of the postcard.

The area is _____ square centimeters.

7. A rectangular field is 1000 meters long and 800 meters wide. How many square meters are in that field?

There are _____ square meters in the field.

1.	2.
3.	4.
5.	6.
7.	

Perfect score: 7   My score: _____

Volume

To determine the *volume measure* (V) of a rectangular solid, find the product of the measure of its *length* (l), the measure of its *width* (w), and the measure of its *height* (h).

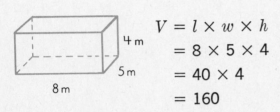

$$V = l \times w \times h$$
$$= 8 \times 5 \times 4$$
$$= 40 \times 4$$
$$= 160$$

The volume is __160__ cubic meters.

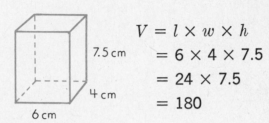

$$V = l \times w \times h$$
$$= 6 \times 4 \times 7.5$$
$$= 24 \times 7.5$$
$$= 180$$

The volume is _____ cubic centimeters.

Find the volume of each rectangular solid below.

	a	*b*	*c*
1.	 2 m, 3 m, 9 m	4 m, 4 m, 4 m	6 m, 4.5 m, 6 m
	_____ cubic meters	_____ cubic meters	_____ cubic meters

2.

  5 cm, 1.5 cm, 2.5 cm

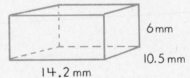 6 mm, 10.5 mm, 14.2 mm

.45 m, .8 m, .5 m

_____ cubic centimeters

_____ cubic millimeters

_____ cubic meter

Find the volume of each rectangular solid described below.

	length	width	height	volume
3.	7 m	6 m	5 m	_____ cubic meters
4.	9.2 cm	4.5 cm	3 cm	_____ cubic centimeters
5.	8.5 mm	8.5 mm	8.5 mm	_____ cubic millimeters
6.	7.2 cm	6.2 cm	5.2 cm	_____ cubic centimeters

Problems

Solve each problem.

1. Find a rectangular room. Measure its length, its width, and its height to the nearest meter. Find the area of the floor and the volume of the room.

length: _____ meters

width: _____ meters

height: _____ meters

floor area: _____ square meters

volume: _____ cubic meters

2. Find a rectangular box. Measure its length, its width, and its height to the nearest centimeter. Find the area of the box top and the volume of the box.

length: _____ centimeters

width: _____ centimeters

height: _____ centimeters

top area: _____ square centimeters

volume: _____ cubic centimeters

3. A shipping crate is 1.2 meters high, .8 meter wide, and 2.5 meters long. Find the volume of the crate.

The volume is _____ cubic meters.

4. A book is 28 centimeters long, 21 centimeters wide, and 1 centimeter thick. How much space does the book occupy?

It occupies _____ cubic centimeters of space.

5. A hole was dug 12.5 meters long, 10.5 meters wide, and 2 meters deep. How many cubic meters of earth were removed?

_____ cubic meters of earth were removed.

1.

2.

3.

4.

5.

Capacity

A box this size can hold **1 milliliter.**

A teaspoon can hold about 5 milliliters.

A **1-liter** bottle can hold 1000 milliliters.

| 1 liter = 1000 milliliters (ml) |
| 1000 liters = 1 kiloliter (kl) |

| 1 ml = .001 liter |
| 1 liter = .001 kl |

Solve each problem.

1. Suppose you drank 5 liters of milk each week. How many milliliters would that be?

That would be _____ milliliters of milk.

2. Each can holds 4 liters of paint. How many liters of paint are in 6 such cans?

_____ liters are in six cans.

3. Each bottle holds 40 milliliters of vanilla. How many such bottles can be filled from 1 liter of vanilla?

_____ bottles can be filled.

4. There are 8000 liters of water in a pool. How many kiloliters of water are in that pool?

_____ kiloliters of water are in that pool.

5. A ship is carrying 480 barrels of oil. Each barrel contains 200 liters of oil. How many liters of oil is the ship carrying?

The ship is carrying _____ liters of oil.

1.	2.
3.	**4.**
5.	

Units of Capacity

65 liters = _____?_____ ml   5.2 liters = _____?_____ kl

1 liter = 1000 ml   1 liter = .001 kl
(65 × 1) liters = (65 × 1000) ml   (5.2 × 1) liters = (5.2 × .001) kl

65 liters = __65,000__ ml   5.2 liters = __.0052__ kl

Complete the following.

	a	*b*
1.	7 liters = _____ ml	.5 liter = _____ ml
2.	5 ml = _____ liter	4500 ml = _____ liters
3.	7.5 kl = _____ liters	2.54 kl = _____ liters
4.	600 liters = _____ kl	7.5 liters = _____ kl
5.	3.4 liters = _____ ml	300 ml = _____ liter
6.	3 kl = _____ liters	300 liters = _____ kl
7.	.6 liter = _____ kl	24 kl = _____ liters
8.	47 ml = _____ liter	.75 liter = _____ ml

Solve.

9. Consider filling the tank shown with water. How many milliliters would the tank hold? How many liters? (Hint: A 1 cubic-centimeter container can hold 1 milliliter of water.)

25 cm
20 cm
40 cm

The tank would hold _____ milliliters.

The tank would hold _____ liters.

Weight

NAME _____

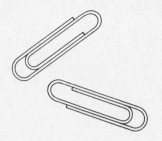

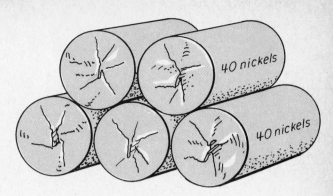

2 paper clips weigh about **1 gram** (g).

1 nickel weighs about 5 grams.

200 nickels weigh about 1000 grams or **1 kilogram** (kg).

1 g = 1000 milligrams (mg)	1 mg = .001 g
1 kg = 1000 g	1 g = .001 kg

Solve each problem.

1. There are 100 paper clips in a box. How many grams would a box of paper clips weigh?

It would weigh _____ grams.

2. There are 20 boxes of paper clips in a carton. How many grams would a carton of paper clips weigh?

The carton would weigh _____ grams.

3. How many grams would a roll of 40 nickels weigh?

The roll would weigh _____ grams.

4. How many nickels would weigh 5 kilograms?

_____ nickels would weigh 5 kilograms.

5. A truck is hauling 6 crates. Each crate weighs 35 kilograms. How much do all the crates weigh?

They weigh _____ kilograms.

1.	2.
3.	4.
5.	

Units of Weight

73 kg = _____?_____ g   54 mg = _____?_____ g

1 kg = 1000 g   1 mg = .001 g
(73 × 1) kg = (73 × 1000) g   (54 × 1) mg = (54 × .001) g

73 kg = ____73,000____ g   54 mg = ____.054____ g

Complete the following.

	a	*b*

1. 8 kg = _____ g   7.5 kg = _____ g

2. 4500 mg = _____ g   38 g = _____ kg

3. 6 g = _____ mg   640 mg = _____ g

4. .05 kg = _____ g   4.5 kg = _____ g

5. .007 kg = _____ g   7000 g = _____ kg

6. 5.5 g = _____ mg   .21 g = _____ mg

7. .4 kg = _____ g   345 g = _____ kg

8. 607 mg = _____ g   8.9 g = _____ mg

9. 52 g = _____ mg   975 g = _____ kg

Solve.

10. Consider this tank filled with water. Assume that 1 liter of water weighs 1 kilogram. How many kilograms would the water in the tank weigh?

The water would weigh _____ kilograms.

TEST—Metric Measurement

Complete the following.

	a	b
1.	9 m = _____ mm	365 mm = _____ m
2.	7.2 m = _____ cm	8.4 cm = _____ m
3.	26 km = _____ m	17 m = _____ km
4.	4.51 liters = _____ ml	65 ml = _____ liter
5.	6.8 kl = _____ liters	3500 liters = _____ kl
6.	.9 kg = _____ g	785 g = _____ kg
7.	2 g = _____ mg	.998 kg = _____ g
8.	1500 m = _____ km	.45 kg = _____ g

Find the area of each rectangle.

a   b

9.

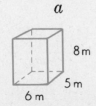
4.5 cm
5.6 cm

2.8 km
3.5 km

_____ square centimeters   _____ square kilometers

Find the volume of each rectangular solid.

a   b

10.

8 m
5 m
6 m

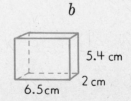
5.4 cm
2 cm
6.5 cm

_____ cubic meters   _____ cubic centimeters

PRE-TEST—Measurement

Complete the following.

	a	b

1. 3 feet = _____ inches   48 inches = _____ feet

2. 6 yards = _____ feet   24 feet = _____ yards

3. 2 miles = _____ feet   3 miles = _____ yards

4. 3 pints = _____ cups   14 cups = _____ pints

5. 7 quarts = _____ pints   8 quarts = _____ gallons

6. 2 pounds = _____ ounces   2000 pounds = _____ ton

7. 6 minutes = _____ seconds   180 seconds = _____ minutes

8. 48 hours = _____ days   120 minutes = _____ hours

9. 4 feet 8 inches = _____ inches

10. 3 gallons 3 quarts = _____ quarts

11. 2 pounds 6 ounces = _____ ounces

12. 2 minutes 30 seconds = _____ seconds

Find the area of each figure.

	a	b

13.

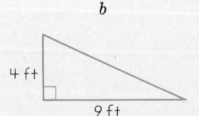

_____ square inches   _____ square feet

Solve.

14. A shoe box is 6 inches wide, 11 inches long, and 5 inches high. Find the volume of the box.

The volume is _____ cubic inches.

SPECTRUM MATHEMATICS,
Green Book–Second Edition

Perfect score: 23   My score: _____

Length

1 foot (ft) = 12 inches (in) 1 yard (yd) = 3 ft 1 yd = 36 in 1 mile (mi) = 5280 ft	1 in = $\frac{1}{12}$ ft 1 ft = $\frac{1}{3}$ yd 1 in = $\frac{1}{36}$ yd 1 mi = 1760 yd

36 in = _____?_____ ft   6 ft 4 in = _____?_____ in

$1 \text{ in} = \frac{1}{12} \text{ ft}$ $1 \text{ ft} = 12 \text{ in}$

$(36 \times 1) \text{ in} = (36 \times \frac{1}{12}) \text{ ft}$ $6 \text{ ft} = (6 \times 12) \text{ or } 72 \text{ in}$

$6 \text{ ft } 4 \text{ in} = (72 + 4) \text{ in}$

36 in = _____3_____ ft

6 ft 4 in = _____76_____ in

Complete the following.

	a	*b*
1.	6 ft = _____ in	60 in = _____ ft
2.	9 yd = _____ ft	12 ft = _____ yd
3.	5 yd = _____ in	144 in = _____ yd
4.	3 mi = _____ ft	3 mi = _____ yd
5.	5 yd = _____ ft	18 in = _____ ft
6.	2 mi = _____ ft	5 mi = _____ yd
7.	5 ft 4 in = _____ in	
8.	3 yd 5 in = _____ in	
9.	5 yd 2 ft = _____ ft	
10.	9 ft 6 in = _____ in	
11.	1 mi 750 ft = _____ ft	

Problems

Solve each problem.

1. The top of a doorway is 84 inches above the floor. What is the height of the doorway in feet?

The doorway is _____ feet high.

2. The distance along the foul line from home plate to the right field fence is 336 feet. What is this distance in yards?

This distance is _____ yards.

3. A kite string is 125 yards long. How many feet long is the string?

The string is _____ feet long.

4. A snake is 4 feet 3 inches long. What is the length of the snake in inches?

Its length is _____ inches.

5. A rope is 5 feet 9 inches long. What is the length of the rope in inches?

The rope is _____ inches long.

6. The distance across a street is 15 yards 1 foot. What is this distance in feet?

This distance is _____ feet.

7. A doorway is 2 feet 8 inches wide. What is the width of the doorway in inches?

The doorway is _____ inches wide.

8. Helen is 4 feet 11 inches tall. What is her height in inches?

Helen is _____ inches tall.

9. Jerry is 5 feet 4 inches tall. What is his height in inches?

Jerry is _____ inches tall.

1.	2.
3.	4.
5.	6.
7.	8.
9.	

SPECTRUM MATHEMATICS,
Green Book–Second Edition

Perfect score: 9   My score: _____

Area

To determine the *area measure* (*A*) of a right triangle, find *one half* the product of the measure of its *base* (*b*) and the measure of its *height* (*h*).

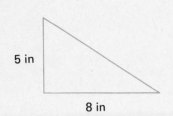

$$A = \tfrac{1}{2} \times b \times h$$
$$= \tfrac{1}{2} \times (8 \times 5)$$
$$= \tfrac{1}{2} \times 40$$
$$= 20$$

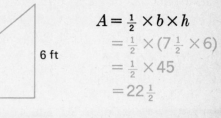

$$A = \tfrac{1}{2} \times b \times h$$
$$= \tfrac{1}{2} \times (7\tfrac{1}{2} \times 6)$$
$$= \tfrac{1}{2} \times 45$$
$$= 22\tfrac{1}{2}$$

The area is ____20____ square inches.

The area is _____ square feet.

Find the area of each right triangle below.

| a | b | c |

1.

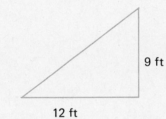

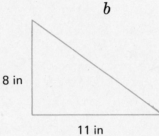

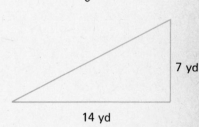

_____ square feet

_____ square inches

_____ square yards

2.

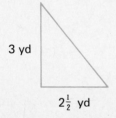

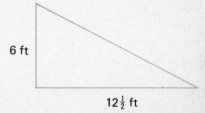

_____ square yards

_____ square inches

_____ square feet

Find the area of each right triangle described below.

	base	height	area
3.	8 ft	9 ft	_____ square feet
4.	7 yd	5 yd	_____ square yards
5.	$4\tfrac{1}{2}$ in	6 in	_____ square inches
6.	5 ft	$3\tfrac{1}{2}$ ft	_____ square feet
7.	$3\tfrac{3}{4}$ in	2 in	_____ square inches

SPECTRUM MATHEMATICS,
Green Book–Second Edition

Perfect score: 11   My score: _____

Problems

Solve each problem.

1. The edges of a flower garden form a right triangle. The base of the triangle is 16 feet and the height is 8 feet. What is the area of the garden?

The area is _____ square feet.

2. A sailboat has a sail which is shaped like a right triangle. The base of the triangle is 14 feet and the height is 20 feet. What is the area of the sail?

The area is _____ square feet.

3. Anne has a piece of poster board which is shaped like a right triangle. The base of the triangle is 28 inches and the height is $16\frac{1}{2}$ inches. What is the area of the piece of poster board?

The area is _____ square inches.

4. Mr. McKee has a patio which is shaped like a right triangle. The base of the triangle is 36 feet and the height is 12 feet. What is the area of the patio?

The area is _____ square feet.

5. A small park is shaped like a right triangle. The base of the triangle is 160 yards and the height is 120 yards. What is the area of the park?

The area is _____ square yards.

6. Nelson has a piece of sheet metal which is shaped like a right triangle. The base of the triangle is 16 inches and the height is $12\frac{1}{2}$ inches. What is the area of the piece of sheet metal?

The area is _____ square inches.

7. Mrs. Jones has a piece of material which is shaped like a right triangle. The base of the triangle is $25\frac{1}{2}$ inches and the height is 18 inches. What is the area of the piece of material?

The area is _____ square inches.

1.

2.

3.

4.

5.

6.

7.

Area and Volume

Find the area of each right triangle or rectangle below.

a   b   c

1.

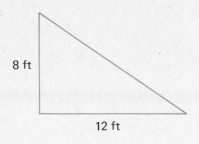

8 ft   12 ft

7 yd   13 yd

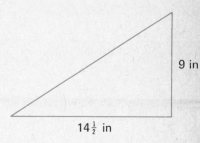

9 in $14\frac{1}{2}$ in

_____ square feet   _____ square yards   _____ square inches

2.

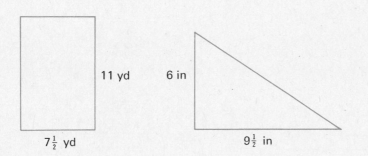

11 yd $7\frac{1}{2}$ yd

6 in $9\frac{1}{2}$ in

$7\frac{1}{2}$ ft $7\frac{1}{2}$ ft

_____ square yards   _____ square inches   _____ square feet

Find the volume of each rectangular solid described below.

	length	width	height	volume
3.	7 yd	5 yd	3 yd	_____ cubic yards
4.	9 in	5 in	$4\frac{1}{2}$ in	_____ cubic inches
5.	6 ft	$3\frac{1}{4}$ ft	9 ft	_____ cubic feet
6.	$5\frac{1}{2}$ yd	3 yd	7 yd	_____ cubic yards
7.	$3\frac{1}{4}$ in	$2\frac{3}{4}$ in	4 in	_____ cubic inches
8.	$6\frac{1}{2}$ ft	5 ft	$4\frac{1}{2}$ ft	_____ cubic feet
9.	3 in	$5\frac{1}{4}$ in	$3\frac{1}{2}$ in	_____ cubic inches
10.	$9\frac{1}{4}$ ft	$8\frac{3}{4}$ ft	5 ft	_____ cubic feet

SPECTRUM MATHEMATICS,
Green Book–Second Edition

Perfect score: 14   My score: _____

Problems

Solve each problem.

1. A basketball court is shaped like a rectangle. The length is 84 feet and the width is 50 feet. What is the area of the court?

The area is _____ square feet.

2. A garden plot is shaped like a right triangle. The base of the triangle is 50 feet and the height is 18 feet. What is the area of the triangle?

The area is _____ square feet.

3. A suitcase is 32 inches long, 16 inches wide, and 6 inches deep. What is the volume of the suitcase?

The volume is _____ cubic inches.

4. Mrs. Langley has a flower bed which is shaped like a right triangle. The base of the triangle is $12\frac{1}{2}$ feet and the height is 6 feet. What is the area of the flower bed?

The area is _____ square feet.

5. A plot of land is shaped like a rectangle. It is 280 yards long and 90 yards wide. What is the area of the plot?

The area is _____ square yards.

6. A box is 9 inches long, $6\frac{1}{2}$ inches wide, and $1\frac{1}{2}$ inches deep. What is the volume of the box?

The volume is _____ cubic inches.

7. A rectangular tabletop is 72 inches long and 36 inches wide. What is the area of the tabletop?

The area is _____ square inches.

8. A brick is 8 inches long, 3 inches wide, and 2 inches high. How much space does the brick occupy?

The brick occupies _____ cubic inches of space.

1.

2.

3.

4.

5.

6.

7.

8.

Capacity

1 pint (pt) = 2 cups	1 cup = $\frac{1}{2}$ pt
1 quart (qt) = 2 pt	1 pt = $\frac{1}{2}$ qt
1 gallon (gal) = 4 qt	1 qt = $\frac{1}{4}$ gal

5 pt = _____?_____ qt

1 pt = $\frac{1}{2}$ qt
5 pt = ($\frac{1}{2}$ × 5) qt

5 pt = _____$2\frac{1}{2}$_____ qt

3 gal 2 qt = _____?_____ qt

1 gal = 4 qt
3 gal = (3 × 4) or 12 qt
3 gal 2 qt = (12 + 2) qt

3 gal 2 qt = _____14_____ qt

Complete the following.

	a	*b*
1.	3 pt = _____ cups	8 cups = _____ pt
2.	5 qt = _____ pt	10 pt = _____ qt
3.	4 gal = _____ qt	11 qt = _____ gal
4.	24 qt = _____ gal	15 pt = _____ qt
5.	2 pt 1 cup = _____ cups	
6.	5 gal 3 qt = _____ qt	
7.	2 qt 1 pt = _____ pt	
8.	4 gal 3 qt = _____ qt	

9. An aquarium holds 3 gallons 3 quarts of water. How many quarts would this be? How many pints? How many cups?

This would be _____ quarts.

This would be _____ pints.

This would be _____ cups.

Weight and Time

1 pound (lb) = 16 ounces (oz) 1 ton = 2000 lb	$1 \text{ oz} = \frac{1}{16} \text{ lb}$
1 minute (min) = 60 seconds (sec) 1 hour = 60 min 1 day = 24 hours	$1 \text{ sec} = \frac{1}{60} \text{ min}$ $1 \text{ min} = \frac{1}{60} \text{ hour}$ $1 \text{ hour} = \frac{1}{24} \text{ day}$

80 oz = _____?_____ lb   1 min 12 sec = _____?_____ sec

$1 \text{ oz} = \frac{1}{16} \text{ lb}$ 1 min = 60 sec
$80 \text{ oz} = (80 \times \frac{1}{16}) \text{ lb}$ 1 min 12 sec = (60 + 12) sec

80 oz = _____5_____ lb   1 min 12 sec = _____72_____ sec

Complete the following.

a $\qquad\qquad\qquad\qquad\qquad\qquad\qquad\qquad$ b

1. 72 lb = _____ oz   80 oz = _____ lb

2. 4 tons = _____ lb   6000 lb = _____ tons

3. 3 min = _____ sec   120 sec = _____ min

4. 5 hours = _____ min   360 min = _____ hours

5. 5 days = _____ hours   144 hours = _____ days

6. 3 lb 12 oz = _____ oz   5 lb 6 oz = _____ oz

7. 3 tons 500 lb = _____ lb

8. 2 hr 45 min = _____ min

9. 4 days 12 hours = _____ hours

10. 4 hours 20 min = _____ min

11. 2 days 8 hours = _____ hours

TEST—Measurement

Complete the following.

	a		b

1. 8 ft = _____ in   72 in = _____ ft

2. 5 yd = _____ ft   30 ft = _____ yd

3. 2 mi = _____ ft   1 mi = _____ yd

4. 6 pt = _____ cups   11 cups = _____ pt

5. 18 qt = _____ pt   12 pt = _____ qt

6. 5 gal = _____ qt   4000 lb = _____ tons

7. 6 lb = _____ oz   32 oz = _____ lb

8. 5 min = _____ sec   120 sec = _____ min

9. 5 ft 10 in = _____ in   2 days = _____ hours

10. 4 gal 1 qt = _____ qt   72 hours = _____ days

11. 4 lb 12 oz = _____ oz

12. 3 hours 30 min = _____ min

Solve.

13. A box is 36 inches long, 12 inches wide, and 10 inches high. Find the volume of the box.

The volume of the box is _____ cubic inches.

Find the area of each figure.

                a   b

14.

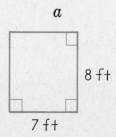

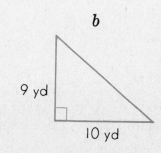

_____ square feet   _____ square yards

PRE-TEST—Per cent

Complete the following.

	a	*b*
1.	$\frac{7}{100}$ = _____ %	$\frac{9}{10}$ = _____ %
2.	$\frac{7}{20}$ = _____ %	$\frac{13}{25}$ = _____ %
3.	.07 = _____ %	.4 = _____ %
4.	.135 = _____ %	1.35 = _____ %

Change each per cent to a decimal.

	a	*b*
5.	6% = _____	67% = _____
6.	6.25% = _____	125% = _____

Change each per cent to a fraction in simplest form.

	a	*b*
7.	9% = _____	20% = _____
8.	45% = _____	56% = _____

Complete the following.

	a	*b*
9.	1% of 59 = _____	10% of 75 = _____
10.	100% of 84 = _____	45% of 89 = _____
11.	75% of 48 = _____	83% of 147 = _____
12.	12% of 180 = _____	7.5% of 840 = _____
13.	6.75% of 500 = _____	8.5% of 96.4 = _____
14.	12.5% of 420 = _____	7% of 79.3 = _____

SPECTRUM MATHEMATICS,
Green Book–Second Edition

Perfect score: 28   My score: _____

Per cent

The symbol % (read **per cent**) means $\frac{1}{100}$ or .01.

$3\% = 3 \times \frac{1}{100}$ or $3\% = 3 \times .01$ $17\% = 17 \times \frac{1}{100}$ or $17\% = 17 \times .01$

$= \underline{\quad \frac{3}{100} \quad}$ $= \underline{\quad .03 \quad}$ $= \underline{\quad\quad\quad}$ $= \underline{\quad\quad\quad}$

Complete the following.

	per cent	fraction	decimal
1.	1%	_____	_____
2.	7%	_____	_____
3.	29%	_____	_____
4.	47%	_____	_____
5.	53%	_____	_____
6.	21%	_____	_____
7.	83%	_____	_____
8.	49%	_____	_____
9.	61%	_____	_____
10.	9%	_____	_____
11.	37%	_____	_____
12.	77%	_____	_____
13.	91%	_____	_____
14.	33%	_____	_____

Per cent and Fractions

Study how a per cent is changed to a fraction or mixed numeral in simplest form.

$$75\% = 75 \times \frac{1}{100}$$

$$= \frac{75}{100}$$

$$= \underline{\quad \frac{3}{4} \quad}$$

$$125\% = 125 \times \frac{1}{100}$$

$$= \frac{125}{100}$$

$$= \frac{5}{4} \text{ or } \underline{\qquad\qquad}$$

Study how a fraction or mixed numeral is changed to a per cent.

$$\frac{1}{2} = \frac{1}{2} \times \frac{50}{50}$$

$$= \frac{50}{100}$$

$$= 50 \times \frac{1}{100}$$

$$= \underline{\quad 50\% \quad}$$

$$1\frac{3}{4} = \frac{7}{4} \times \frac{25}{25}$$

$$= \frac{175}{100}$$

$$= 175 \times \frac{1}{100}$$

$$= \underline{\qquad\qquad}\%$$

Change each of the following to a fraction or mixed numeral in simplest form.

	a	*b*	*c*
1.	25% = _____	45% = _____	160% = _____
2.	65% = _____	120% = _____	24% = _____
3.	78% = _____	55% = _____	260% = _____
4.	70% = _____	144% = _____	86% = _____
5.	95% = _____	40% = _____	180% = _____

Change each of the following to a per cent.

	a	*b*	*c*
6.	$\frac{1}{5} =$ _____	$\frac{3}{4} =$ _____	$\frac{1}{20} =$ _____
7.	$2\frac{7}{50} =$ _____	$\frac{3}{5} =$ _____	$1\frac{1}{5} =$ _____
8.	$\frac{9}{10} =$ _____	$\frac{7}{25} =$ _____	$2\frac{1}{4} =$ _____
9.	$1\frac{3}{5} =$ _____	$\frac{3}{10} =$ _____	$\frac{4}{25} =$ _____
10.	$\frac{7}{20} =$ _____	$\frac{31}{50} =$ _____	$1\frac{2}{5} =$ _____

SPECTRUM MATHEMATICS,
Green Book–Second Edition

Perfect score: 30   My score: _____

Per cent and Decimals

Study how a per cent is changed to a decimal.

$12.5\% = 12.5 \times .01$ $1.25\% = 1.25 \times .01$

$= \underline{\quad .125 \quad}$ $= \underline{\qquad}$

Study how a decimal is changed to a per cent.

$.7 = .70$ $.245 = 24.5 \times .01$
$= 70 \times .01$

$= \underline{\quad 70\% \quad}$ $= \underline{\qquad}\%$

Change each of the following to a decimal.

	a	b	c
1.	$13.5\% = $_____	$37\% = $_____	$6.25\% = $_____
2.	$6.5\% = $_____	$4.75\% = $_____	$2.75\% = $_____
3.	$7\% = $_____	$62.5\% = $_____	$8.5\% = $_____
4.	$32.5\% = $_____	$8.75\% = $_____	$9.5\% = $_____
5.	$8.25\% = $_____	$17.5\% = $_____	$3.75\% = $_____
6.	$.75\% = $_____	$7.25\% = $_____	$1.75\% = $_____

Change each of the following to a per cent.

	a	b	c
7.	$.6 = $_____	$.52 = $_____	$.325 = $_____
8.	$.2475 = $_____	$.8 = $_____	$.65 = $_____
9.	$.145 = $_____	$.1675 = $_____	$.5 = $_____
10.	$.06 = $_____	$.007 = $_____	$.0625 = $_____
11.	$.075 = $_____	$.0075 = $_____	$.005 = $_____
12.	$.9 = $_____	$.19 = $_____	$.385 = $_____

Problems

Solve each problem.

1. Three fourths of the pupils in class are girls. What per cent of the pupils are girls?

_____ of the pupils are girls.

1.

---

2. Mr. Beck received 65% of the votes cast. What fractional part of the votes did he receive?

He received _____ of the votes.

2.

---

3. Marty made a base hit on 25% of his official times at bat. What is his batting average? (Note: Batting averages are usually expressed as thousandths.)

His average is _____.

3.

---

4. Four fifths of the pupils are in the gym. What per cent of the pupils are in the gym?

_____ of the pupils are in the gym.

4.

---

5. A farmer has 45% of a field plowed. Write a fraction to tell how much of the field is plowed.

_____ of the field is plowed.

5.

---

6. The Cubs won 61.5% of their games last year. How can this per cent be expressed as a decimal?

61.5% can be expressed as _____.

6.

---

7. A certain player has a fielding average of .987. How can this fielding average be expressed as a per cent?

This average can be expressed as _____.

7.

---

8. Seven tenths of the customers at the Caribbean Market come in the morning. What per cent of the customers come in the morning?

_____ of the customers come in the morning.

8.

Per cent of a Number

Study how fractions are used to find a per cent of a number.

$$75\% \text{ of } 60 = 75\% \times 60$$
$$= \frac{75}{100} \times 60$$
$$= \frac{3}{4} \times \frac{60}{1}$$
$$= \frac{3 \times 60}{4 \times 1}$$
$$= \frac{180}{4} \text{ or } 45$$

$$125\% \text{ of } 37.5 = 125\% \times 37.5$$
$$= \frac{125}{100} \times 37.5$$
$$= \frac{5}{4} \times \frac{375}{10}$$
$$= \frac{5 \times 375}{4 \times 10}$$
$$= \frac{1875}{40} \text{ or } 46\frac{7}{8}$$

75% of 60 = _____45_____   125% of 37.5 = _____

Write each answer in simplest form.

	a	*b*
1.	6% of 75 = _____	108% of 63.5 = _____
2.	50% of 32 = _____	75% of 12.6 = _____
3.	20% of 68 = _____	25% of 72.8 = _____
4.	5% of 48 = _____	15% of 52.4 = _____
5.	104% of 35 = _____	136% of 7.5 = _____
6.	55% of 5.25 = _____	80% of 160 = _____
7.	166% of 60 = _____	90% of 1.8 = _____
8.	72% of 7.25 = _____	140% of 240 = _____
9.	60% of 9.8 = _____	250% of 90 = _____
10.	100% of 725 = _____	40% of 9.6 = _____

SPECTRUM MATHEMATICS,
Green Book–Second Edition

Perfect score: 20   My score: _____

Problems

Solve each problem.

1. Twenty-five per cent of the workers are on the third shift. There are 132 workers in all. How many of them are on the third shift?

_____ are on the third shift.

2. The enrollment at Franklin School has increased 20% from last year. The enrollment last year was 750. By how many pupils has the enrollment increased?

The enrollment has increased by _____ pupils.

3. Ms. Allan is paid 5% of her total sales. How much would she earn in a week if her total sales were $2800?

She would earn _____.

4. Forty per cent of the class finished their assignment before lunch. There are 25 pupils in the class. How many pupils finished before lunch?

_____ pupils finished before lunch.

5. The excise tax on a certain item is 10% of the sales price. What would be the amount of excise tax on an item which sells for $60?

The excise tax would be _____.

6. It is estimated that a new truck will be worth 75% of its original cost after one year. How much would a 1-year old truck be worth that originally sold for $5600?

The truck would be worth _____.

7. Fifty per cent of the people questioned in a sales survey indicated a preference for Brand X. There were 7,520 people questioned. How many of the people questioned preferred Brand X?

_____ people preferred Brand X.

1.

2.

3.

4.

5.

6.

7.

SPECTRUM MATHEMATICS,
Green Book–Second Edition

Perfect score: 7   My score: _____

Per cent of a Number

Study how decimals are used to find a per cent of a number.

$$34\% \text{ of } 62.3 \dashrightarrow 62.3$$

$$\begin{array}{r} 62.3 \\ \times\,.34 \\ \hline 2492 \\ 18690 \\ \hline 21.182 \end{array}$$

34% of 62.3 = ___21.182___

Complete the following.

	a		*b*	
1.	28% of 62.5 = _____		7.5% of 34 = _____	
2.	73% of 95 = _____		5.5% of 9.6 = _____	
3.	9.5% of 780 = _____		2% of 73.6 = _____	
4.	5% of 8.5 = _____		39% of 420 = _____	
5.	6.25% of 700 = _____		125% of 62.5 = _____	
6.	85% of 672 = _____		7% of 86.4 = _____	
7.	9% of 960 = _____		10% of 95.6 = _____	
8.	140% of 280 = _____		8.5% of 785 = _____	
9.	25% of 386 = _____		18% of 70 = _____	
10.	67% of 18.5 = _____		7.75% of 62.4 = _____	
11.	107% of 600 = _____		8% of 420 = _____	
12.	83% of 840 = _____		106% of 780 = _____	

Problems

Solve each problem.

1. During the sale Mr. Hansen purchased a suit. The suit normally sells for $120. How much money did he save by purchasing the suit during the sale?

He saved _____.

2. Mrs. James purchased a dress at the sale. The regular price on the dress was $48. How much did Mrs. James save by purchasing the dress during the sale?

She saved _____.

3. During the sale, ladies' coats are selling for 75% of the original price. The original price is $98. What is the sale price of the coats?

The sale price is _____.

4. A sales tax of 5% is charged on all purchases. What is the sales tax on a purchase of $78?

The sales tax is _____.

5. Charge-account customers must pay a finance charge of 1.5% of their unpaid balance. What is the finance charge to a customer who has an unpaid balance of $82?

The finance charge is _____.

1.

2.

3.

4.

5.

SPECTRUM MATHEMATICS,
Green Book–Second Edition

Perfect score: 5   My score: _____

TEST—Per cent

Complete the following. Write each fraction in simplest form.

	fraction	decimal	per cent
1.	$\frac{3}{100}$	_____	_____
2.	$\frac{1}{4}$	_____	_____
3.	$\frac{7}{20}$	_____	_____
4.	_____	.06	_____
5.	_____	.39	_____
6.	_____	.125	_____
7.	_____	_____	5%
8.	_____	_____	28%
9.	_____	_____	75%
10.	_____	_____	90%

Complete the following.

11. 25% of 64 = _____

12. 80% of 78 = _____

13. 6.25% of 700 = _____

14. 32.5% of 62.4 = _____

15. 8.5% of 96.8 = _____

SPECTRUM MATHEMATICS,
Green Book–Second Edition

Perfect score: 25   My score: _____

PRE-TEST—Review

Add or subtract.

	a	b	c	d	e
1.	$\begin{array}{r} 1897 \\ +698 \\ \hline \end{array}$	$\begin{array}{r} 37.51 \\ +48.67 \\ \hline \end{array}$	$\begin{array}{r} 3.851 \\ 12.63 \\ +6.417 \\ \hline \end{array}$	$\begin{array}{r} 9\frac{3}{8} \\ +2\frac{3}{8} \\ \hline \end{array}$	$\begin{array}{r} 6\frac{7}{8} \\ +2\frac{2}{3} \\ \hline \end{array}$

2.	$\begin{array}{r} 6785 \\ -1434 \\ \hline \end{array}$	$\begin{array}{r} 86.767 \\ -14.132 \\ \hline \end{array}$	$\begin{array}{r} 187.42 \\ -34.567 \\ \hline \end{array}$	$\begin{array}{r} 9\frac{7}{8} \\ -2\frac{1}{4} \\ \hline \end{array}$	$\begin{array}{r} 6\frac{5}{6} \\ -3\frac{9}{10} \\ \hline \end{array}$

Multiply or divide.

	a	b	c	d
3.	$\begin{array}{r} 705 \\ \times 369 \\ \hline \end{array}$	$\begin{array}{r} 3.141 \\ \times 4.3 \\ \hline \end{array}$	$37\overline{)4735}$	$.149\overline{)3.7697}$

4. $\quad \dfrac{4}{7} \times \dfrac{5}{6} \qquad\qquad 1\dfrac{2}{3} \times 2\dfrac{3}{4} \qquad\qquad \dfrac{6}{7} \div \dfrac{2}{3} \qquad\qquad 1\dfrac{3}{4} \div 3\dfrac{1}{5}$

Complete the following. – Do two, the other four are extra

	a	b
5.	6 m = _____ mm	10% of 75 = _____
6.	4 min 9 sec = _____ sec	6.5% of 300 = _____
7.	5 gal = _____ qt	25% of 250 = _____

Addition

Add.

	a	*b*	*c*	*d*	*e*
1.	73 +25	146 +239	2431 +387	3453 +2734	34567 +18132
2.	37 28 +18	124 425 +237	1423 362 +3474	3124 2435 +769	34125 7345 +28658
3.	.7 +.2	7.3 +3.8	.25 +.63	64.87 +25.36	2.843 +7.106
4.	2.3 1.6 +.7	23.4 18.3 +5.7	7.23 36.7 +5.25	28.761 18.875 +2.25	48.147 83.52 +42.975

Write each answer in simplest form.

	a	*b*	*c*	*d*
5.	$\frac{3}{7}$ $+\frac{2}{7}$	$\frac{3}{9}$ $+\frac{4}{9}$	$\frac{3}{8}$ $+\frac{3}{8}$	$\frac{7}{10}$ $+\frac{8}{10}$
6.	$\frac{3}{4}$ $+\frac{1}{8}$	$\frac{1}{5}$ $+\frac{2}{3}$	$\frac{2}{3}$ $+\frac{3}{4}$	$\frac{2}{5}$ $+\frac{3}{4}$
7.	$2\frac{2}{3}$ $+\frac{1}{8}$	$\frac{3}{5}$ $+2\frac{2}{7}$	$9\frac{1}{3}$ $2\frac{5}{6}$ $+2\frac{1}{4}$	$5\frac{1}{6}$ $3\frac{2}{3}$ $+3\frac{3}{4}$

Problems

Solve each problem.

1. There were 163 painters, 149 carpenters, 94 bricklayers, 67 plumbers, and 101 electricians present at a building trades meeting. How many workers were present in all?

2. Mr. Williams purchased a shirt for $9.98, a pair of slacks for $24.50, and a tie for $4.75. What was the total amount of his purchases?

3. The McDonel's purchased a $6\frac{3}{4}$-pound ham, a $3\frac{1}{2}$-pound roast, and $2\frac{1}{4}$ pounds of ground beef. How many pounds of meat did they purchase?

4. An auto racer obtained a top speed of 135.3 miles per hour. With some special equipment, this speed can be increased by 7.5 miles per hour. What would the racer's top speed be with the special equipment?

5. Two boards are placed end to end. One is $32\frac{1}{4}$ inches long and the other $34\frac{7}{8}$ inches long. What is the combined length of the boards?

6. During a 4-day period Mr. Mason drove 18.7 miles, 25.7 miles, 32.9 miles, and 16.6 miles. How many miles did he drive during the period?

7. A relief pitcher pitched $2\frac{1}{3}$ innings Monday, $1\frac{2}{3}$ innings Wednesday, and $3\frac{2}{3}$ innings Saturday. How many innings did the player pitch those 3 days?

1.

2.

3.

4.

5.

6.

7.

Subtraction

Subtract.

	a	b	c	d	e
1.	5 7 −3	2 5 4 −4 3	4 1 2 4 −1 0 2	6 7 8 5 −1 1 3 2	5 4 3 2 2 −3 1 1 2
2.	6 9 −1 4	6 7 8 −1 6 7	2 5 7 6 −1 4 2 7	6 7 5 4 −3 2 9 2	3 7 1 2 5 −1 4 0 1 8
3.	7 8 −2 9	8 3 7 −2 2 9	7 8 7 6 −4 9 2 2	8 7 5 7 −7 9 9 8	6 7 8 5 2 −2 8 9 0 9
4.	.7 −.2	1.8 9 −.9 2	.7 6 −.1 9	6.7 5 2 −.2 8 1	1.2 3 4 −.1 2 5
5.	2.5 −1.6	1 2.3 4 −7.5 3	1 2.5 6 −4.2 7	7.5 6 3 −1.2 7 5	7 8.6 7 5 −1 5.6 8 9

Write each answer in simplest form.

	a	b	c	d
6.	$\dfrac{6}{7}$ $-\dfrac{3}{7}$	$\dfrac{7}{9}$ $-\dfrac{5}{9}$	$\dfrac{11}{12}$ $-\dfrac{7}{12}$	$\dfrac{15}{16}$ $-\dfrac{7}{16}$
7.	$\dfrac{3}{4}$ $-\dfrac{2}{3}$	$\dfrac{9}{10}$ $-\dfrac{2}{5}$	$\dfrac{2}{3}$ $-\dfrac{3}{8}$	$\dfrac{11}{12}$ $-\dfrac{5}{9}$
8.	$2\dfrac{1}{2}$ $-\dfrac{3}{4}$	$4\dfrac{2}{3}$ $-\dfrac{7}{8}$	$8\dfrac{1}{3}$ $-6\dfrac{3}{4}$	$6\dfrac{1}{4}$ $-3\dfrac{3}{5}$

Perfect score: 37   My score: _____

Problems

Solve each problem.

1. In the election for mayor, Jennings received 9,775 votes and Vaughn received 6,989 votes. How many more votes did Jennings receive than Vaughn?

Jennings received _____ more votes.

2. An engine used 16.9 liters of gasoline last week. This week it used 18.7 liters. How much more gasoline did it use this week than last week?

It used _____ more liters this week.

3. A $28\frac{3}{4}$-inch piece of rope is to be cut from a rope which is $72\frac{1}{2}$ inches long. How much rope will be left?

_____ inches of rope will be left.

4. Ten years ago the population of Oakwood was 91,475. Today the population is 135,924. How much has the population of Oakwood increased during the ten-year period?

The population has increased _____.

5. Last season a baseball player had a batting average of .289. This season the player's average is .314. What is the difference between these averages?

The difference is _____.

6. Charles weighs $107\frac{1}{2}$ pounds. His younger brother weighs $98\frac{3}{4}$ pounds. What is the difference between their weights?

The difference is _____ pounds.

7. During a sale Mrs. McGill purchased a dress for $29.88. The dress normally sells for $37.50. How much money did Mrs. McGill save by purchasing the dress at the sale?

She saved $_____.

1.
2.
3.
4.
5.
6.
7.

Multiplication

Multiply.

	a	b	c	d	e
1.	3 2 ×7	3 2 4 ×2	5 7 8 ×8	3 2 1 3 ×3	6 7 5 7 ×9
2.	2 4 ×2 4	1 7 8 ×5 7	4 0 3 7 ×6 9	6 7 8 ×3 0 5	4 5 7 9 ×6 1 4
3.	4 2 ×1.7	1 2.8 ×6.2	3.1 4 ×5.7	1.7 8 ×3.6 4	7.5 4 3 ×3.7

Write each answer in simplest form.

	a	b	c	d
4.	$\frac{1}{2} \times \frac{3}{4}$	$\frac{4}{7} \times \frac{4}{5}$	$\frac{7}{8} \times \frac{5}{6}$	$\frac{2}{7} \times \frac{7}{8}$
5.	$2 \times \frac{3}{4}$	$\frac{7}{8} \times 5$	$6\frac{1}{2} \times \frac{7}{8}$	$1\frac{3}{4} \times 2\frac{2}{3}$

Problems

Solve each problem.

1. A truck is carrying 164 cartons of merchandise. Each carton weighs 55 pounds. What is the total weight of the merchandise?

2. To pay for an installment purchase, Mr. Ford is to pay $31.78 a month for 12 months. What is the total amount of these payments?

3. Mrs. Loving purchased six $1\frac{1}{4}$-pound loaves of bread. What was the total weight of the bread that she purchased?

4. Miss Holloway has 12 books of trading stamps. There are 1,200 stamps in each book. How many stamps does she have in all?

5. What would be the total cost of 3 pairs of slacks at $18.95 each?

6. A light truck can carry $\frac{3}{4}$-ton of gravel. The truck is now $\frac{2}{3}$ loaded. What part of a ton is now loaded on the truck?

7. Gasoline costs $.18 a liter. What would be the cost of 62.5 liters of gasoline?

8. It is $1\frac{1}{4}$ miles around Memorial Park. Dolly ran $\frac{2}{3}$ of the way around the park. How far did she run?

1.

2.

3.

4.

5.

6.

7.

8.

Division

Divide.

	a	*b*	*c*	*d*	*e*
1.	4)76	5)184	6)967	8)4968	7)8953

	a	*b*	*c*	*d*	*e*
2.	25)375	67)4675	24)974	83)13861	43)36952

	a	*b*	*c*	*d*	*e*
3.	.6)189	.27)243	5.9)20.06	.61)1.708	.049)2.009

Write each answer in simplest form.

	a	*b*	*c*	*d*
4.	$\frac{1}{2} \div \frac{3}{4}$	$2 \div \frac{7}{8}$	$\frac{8}{9} \div 4$	$1\frac{3}{8} \div \frac{2}{3}$

	a	*b*	*c*	*d*
5.	$\frac{5}{6} \div 1\frac{1}{3}$	$2 \div 3\frac{1}{7}$	$8\frac{3}{8} \div 3$	$3\frac{3}{4} \div 1\frac{2}{3}$

Problems

Solve each problem.

1. Harriet checked out a library book which contained 276 pages. She plans to read the same number of pages each day. How many pages must she read each day in order to complete the book in 6 days?

1.

2. Mr. Andrews has driven his car 8,239 miles in 11 months. He drives the same number of miles each month. How many miles does he drive each month?

2.

3. There are 83,189 items to be packed. Twenty-four items can be packed in each case. How many cases can be filled? How many items will be left over?

3.

4. The total cost of 8 spark plugs was $10.32. What was the cost of each spark plug?

4.

5. In traveling 194.4 kilometers, Mrs. Lane's car used 36 liters of gasoline. How many kilometers were traveled for each liter of gasoline used?

5.

6. There are 9 gallons of punch in a large container. How many $\frac{3}{4}$-gallon jugs can be filled by using the punch from the large container?

6.

7. A ribbon $6\frac{3}{4}$ feet long is to be cut into 4 pieces. Each piece is to be the same length. What will be the length of each piece?

7.

Measurement

Complete the following.

	a	*b*
1.	9 m = _____ mm	780 mm = _____ m
2.	4.3 m = _____ cm	6.8 cm = _____ m
3.	16 km = _____ m	419 m = _____ km
4.	7 liters = _____ ml	6500 ml = _____ liters
5.	2 kl = _____ liters	918 liters = _____ kl
6.	8.4 kg = _____ g	1350 g = _____ kg
7.	4 g = _____ kg	300 g = _____ kg
8.	5 ft = _____ in	3 ft 9 in = _____ in
9.	2 yd = _____ ft	3 yd 2 ft = _____ ft
10.	6 pt = _____ cups	3 pt 1 cup = _____ cups
11.	9 qt = _____ gal	4 gal 3 qt = _____ qt
12.	5 lb = _____ oz	7 lb 12 oz = _____ oz
13.	6 hours = _____ min	5 hours 15 min = _____ min
14.	4 days = _____ hours	3 days 8 hours = _____ hours

Find the area of the rectangle and of the right
triangle. Find the volume of the rectangular solid.

	a	*b*	*c*

15.

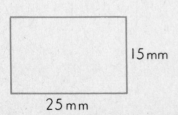

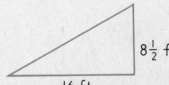

_____ square   _____ square   _____ cubic
millimeters   feet   centimeters

SPECTRUM MATHEMATICS,
Green Book–Second Edition

Perfect score: 31   My score: _____

Per cent

Complete the following. Write each fraction in simplest form.

	fraction	decimal	per cent
1.	$\frac{1}{4}$	_____	_____
2.	$\frac{1}{2}$	_____	_____
3.	$\frac{3}{5}$	_____	_____
4.	_____	.4	_____
5.	_____	.03	_____
6.	_____	.625	_____
7.	_____	_____	7%
8.	_____	_____	37.5%
9.	_____	_____	95%

Complete the following.

10. 10% of 240 = _____

11. 50% of 348 = _____

12. 25% of 484 = _____

13. 6.5% of 350 = _____

14. 8.75% of 480 = _____

15. 12.5% of 840 = _____

16. 7.5% of 640 = _____

SPECTRUM MATHEMATICS,
Green Book–Second Edition

Perfect score: 25   My score: _____

Problems

Solve each problem.

1. A certain basketball player is 6 feet 9 inches tall. What is the player's height in inches?

His height is _____ inches.

2. At the Petroleum Building, 25% of the workers use the Rapid Transit System. There are 1,248 workers in all. How many use the Rapid Transit System?

_____ workers use the system.

3. A rectangular piece of cardboard is 36 centimeters long and 12.5 centimeters wide. Find the area of the cardboard.

The area is _____ square centimeters.

4. Yesterday the school lunchroom served 624 pints of milk. How many quarts of milk was this?

It was _____ quarts of milk.

5. Mrs. Kukla has a flower garden which is shaped like a right triangle. The base of the triangle is 16 feet and the height is $8\frac{1}{2}$ feet. What is the area of the triangle?

The area is _____ square feet.

6. Eugene has a box that is 28 inches long, $16\frac{1}{2}$ inches wide, and $8\frac{1}{2}$ inches deep. Find the volume of the box.

The volume is _____ cubic inches.

7. The state sales tax is 5%. At that rate, what would be the sales tax on a purchase of $78?

The sales tax would be $_____.

8. The ball game lasted 2 hours and 30 minutes. How many minutes did the game last?

The game lasted _____ minutes.

1.
2.
3.
4.
5.
6.
7.
8.

SPECTRUM MATHEMATICS,
Green Book–Second Edition

Perfect score: 8   My score: _____

TEST—Review

Complete the following as indicated.

	a	*b*	*c*	*d*
1.	$\begin{array}{r} 8\,7.5\,7 \\ -2\,4.8\,9\,4 \\ \hline \end{array}$	$\begin{array}{r} 6\frac{5}{8} \\ -4\frac{5}{6} \\ \hline \end{array}$	$\begin{array}{r} 3\,1\,5.4\,2 \\ 1\,5.3\,7\,3 \\ +6\,8\,4.1\,2 \\ \hline \end{array}$	$\begin{array}{r} 9\frac{3}{8} \\ +4\frac{1}{2} \\ \hline \end{array}$
2.	$\begin{array}{r} 6\,2\,5 \\ \times 4\,0\,7 \\ \hline \end{array}$	$25\overline{)7\,8\,7}$	$\begin{array}{r} 1.4\,1\,4 \\ \times 7.4 \\ \hline \end{array}$	$3.7\overline{)1\,6.6\,5}$
3.	$\frac{5}{8}\times\frac{3}{4}$	$\frac{7}{8}\div\frac{2}{3}$	$1\frac{1}{3}\times 4\frac{5}{8}$	$4\frac{2}{3}\div\frac{3}{5}$

Complete the following.

	a	*b*
4.	5 kg = _____ g	75% of 32 = _____
5.	24 qt = _____ gal	5.5% of 435 = _____

Find the area of each rectangle described below.

	length	width	area
6.	13 cm	9 cm	_____ square centimeters
7.	$6\frac{1}{2}$ cm	$5\frac{1}{2}$ cm	_____ square centimeters

Find the area of each right triangle described below.

	base	height	area
8.	7.5 m	8 m	_____ square meters
9.	9 in	$6\frac{1}{4}$ in	_____ square inches

Answers for
SPECTRUM MATHEMATICS (Green Book, Second Edition)
(Answers for Pre-Tests and Tests are given on pages 159–160.)

Page 1

1. 435; 201; 636   2. 435; 123; 312   3. 759

Page 3

	a	b	c	d	e	f
1.	39	27	53	45	59	87
2.	59	78	78	78	69	78
3.	81	63	77	146	103	148
4.	124	151	131	111	102	152
5.	59	80	115	127	68	124
6.	186	134	109	178	180	216

Page 4

	a	b	c	d	e	f
1.	54	94	60	69	29	38
2.	43	43	54	25	10	31
3.	25	48	34	19	7	17
4.	127	156	268	107	226	59
5.	70	191	286	93	390	485
6.	87	283	376	79	437	549

Page 5

	a	b	c	d	e
1.	588	846	858	1267	1422
2.	6408	8343	9372	8733	11356
3.	78553	81378	97121	91967	91170
4.	1262	11411	12241	91272	73549
5.	60321	80121	9023	46838	53757
6.	1684	15287	13564	104566	103743
7.	42869	48277	76063	85022	79379

Page 6

1. 528; 746; 1274   4. 15342
2. 5281; 7390; 12671   5. 94400
3. 42165; 34895; 77060   6. 86889

Page 7

	a	b	c	d	e
1.	412	217	351	179	404
2.	3902	1929	4895	1889	849
3.	3031	1434	2088	2314	5048
4.	48913	39516	48917	53750	24321
5.	20937	23476	38708	34809	12299
6.	26035	23761	65995	60693	441

Page 8

1. 500; 385; 115   3. 1464   5. 36332
2. 1516; 842; 674   4. 48459   6. 13687

Page 9

	a	b	c	d	e	f
1.	38	53	58	73	139	135
2.	55	51	9	66	58	165
3.	887	965	877	661	1112	1622
4.	281	508	281	1788	1788	998
5.	8699	6840	10087	11324	11040	
6.	5114	4079	5670	3883	16809	
7.	73545	87550	75520	90417	95732	
8.	42101	48075	10244	29289	7718	
9.	99	1493	11796	88088	84788	

Page 10

1. add; 1687   4. subtract; 3695
2. subtract; 427   5. add; 61357
3. add; 3043   6. add; 60114

Page 13

	a	b	c	d	e	f	g	h
1.	0	0	0	0	7	6	1	5
2.	16	4	8	14	12	10	6	18
3.	27	21	15	0	3	18	12	9
4.	16	12	20	32	28	0	36	4
5.	40	10	35	25	20	15	5	0
6.	48	12	54	42	36	30	6	18
7.	63	49	42	0	7	35	56	28
8.	0	40	64	72	32	24	48	56
9.	27	81	72	9	18	63	54	36

Page 14

	a	b	c	d	e	f	g	h
1.	2	3	5	4	6	9	8	1
2.	9	6	7	8	4	5	2	1
3.	0	5	3	4	8	6	1	7
4.	5	2	1	3	8	6	9	4
5.	6	9	0	2	5	3	8	1
6.	5	4	7	1	2	6	9	8
7.	0	3	2	8	7	9	5	4
8.	2	0	7	9	6	4	3	5
9.	5	3	4	7	1	9	0	6

Page 15

	a	b	c	d	e
1.	96	92	246	624	570
2.	842	492	723	2505	954
3.	2349	4304	3810	6678	4257
4.	2066	9648	9516	10028	9771
5.	8868	40166	43434	32304	35415

Page 16

1. 24; 5; 120   3. 365; 3; 1095   5. 6802
2. 77; 7; 539   4. 3875   6. 20755

Page 17

	a	b	c	d	e
1.	1197	1536	4725	6480	11592
2.	14337	76820	50328	172044	651636
3.	88382	300048	90272	537536	
4.	1243380	2411010	1889280	3449412	

Page 18

1. 28; 35; 980   4. 104224
2. 47; 19; 893   5. 105264
3. 321; 52; 16692   6. 525600

Page 19

	a	b	c	d	e
1.	23	19 r1	24	19 r1	135
2.	75	98 r2	1346 r4	526 r5	709

Page 20

1. 92; 5; 18   3. 305   5. 3258
2. 258   4. 68; 1   6. 384; 3

Page 21

	a	b	c	d	e
1.	32 r10	27	45 r9	26 r25	92
2.	142 r27	346 r10	356 r49	525 r25	351

Page 22

1. 988; 26; 38   3. 309; 25   5. 225
2. 41; 3   4. 75   6. 752; 28

Page 23

	a	b	c	d	e
1.	245	1735	3080	12942	29436
2.	3145	2592	32844	10982	117612
3.	20856	222390	76245	526787	577382
4.	17 r12	12 r32	38	122 r4	157
5.	206 r2	63 r3	425	468 r11	1062 r17

Page 24

1. multiply; 48750   4. divide; 77; 15
2. divide; 7   5. divide; 123; 10
3. multiply; 43680   6. multiply; 524160

Page 27

	a	b	c	d			a	b
1.	$\frac{1}{2}$	$\frac{3}{4}$	$\frac{1}{3}$	$\frac{1}{5}$		6.	$\frac{4}{5}$	$\frac{7}{8}$
2.	$\frac{3}{5}$	$\frac{3}{8}$	$\frac{5}{6}$	$\frac{5}{8}$		7.	$\frac{5}{6}$	$\frac{7}{9}$
						8.	$\frac{6}{7}$	$\frac{3}{5}$

	a	b			a	b
3.	$\frac{1}{2}$	$\frac{3}{8}$		9.	$\frac{5}{8}$	$\frac{2}{7}$
4.	$\frac{2}{3}$	$\frac{4}{7}$		10.	$\frac{9}{10}$	$\frac{4}{9}$
5.	$\frac{3}{4}$	$\frac{3}{7}$				

Page 28

	a	b	c	d			a	b	c
1.	$\frac{1}{5}$	4	3; $\frac{3}{4}$	$9\frac{1}{3}$		4.	$2\frac{1}{2}$	$1\frac{4}{5}$	$3\frac{1}{2}$
2.	$\frac{5}{2}$	5	6; $\frac{2}{5}$	$8\frac{7}{8}$		5.	$2\frac{1}{4}$	$1\frac{1}{5}$	$2\frac{2}{3}$
3.	$\frac{1}{8}$	2	3; $\frac{1}{3}$	$5\frac{3}{7}$		6.	$4\frac{2}{3}$	$3\frac{1}{3}$	$3\frac{2}{5}$

	a	b	c
7.	less than 1	greater than 1	equal to 1
8.	less than 1	equal to 1	greater than 1
9.	less than 1	greater than 1	greater than 1

Page 29

	a	b	c	d
1.	$\frac{4}{5}$	$\frac{7}{8}$	$\frac{4}{7}$	$\frac{4}{5}$
2.	$\frac{5}{6}$	$\frac{4}{7}$	$\frac{3}{8}$	$\frac{3}{4}$
3.	$\frac{7}{10}$	$\frac{5}{12}$	$\frac{9}{11}$	$\frac{11}{15}$

	a	b	c	d	e	f
4.	$\frac{5}{6}$	$\frac{7}{8}$	$\frac{3}{5}$	$\frac{9}{10}$	$\frac{11}{12}$	$\frac{4}{11}$
5.	$\frac{3}{5}$	$\frac{6}{7}$	$\frac{5}{8}$	$\frac{7}{10}$	$\frac{11}{15}$	$\frac{7}{12}$

Page 30

	a	b	c			a	b	c
1.	$\frac{21}{8}$	$\frac{13}{5}$	$\frac{11}{3}$		3.	$\frac{55}{8}$	$\frac{59}{10}$	$\frac{161}{12}$
2.	$\frac{37}{10}$	$\frac{32}{3}$	$\frac{29}{2}$		4.	$\frac{29}{6}$	$\frac{31}{4}$	$\frac{107}{12}$

Page 31

	a	b	c	d
1.	$\frac{1}{6}$	$\frac{3}{8}$	$\frac{1}{12}$	$\frac{3}{10}$
2.	$\frac{9}{20}$	$\frac{12}{35}$	$\frac{8}{15}$	$\frac{15}{56}$
3.	$\frac{15}{15}$	$\frac{1}{16}$	$\frac{1}{28}$	$\frac{21}{40}$
4.	$\frac{18}{35}$	$\frac{2}{27}$	$\frac{15}{56}$	$\frac{6}{35}$
5.	$\frac{49}{64}$	$\frac{4}{9}$	$\frac{8}{27}$	$\frac{24}{35}$
6.	$\frac{40}{63}$	$\frac{5}{24}$	$\frac{25}{42}$	$\frac{15}{64}$

Page 32

	a	b	c	d
1.		4	8	9
2.		24	30	25
3.	8	80	10	15

Page 33

		c	d
1.	1,2,3,6 / 1,2,5,10	1,2	2
2.	1,5 / 1,2,4,8	1	1
3.	1,2,3,4,6,12 / 1,3,5,15	1,3	3
4.	1,2,5,10 / 1,2,4,5,10,20	1,2,5,10	10
5.	1,2,7,14 / 1,2,4,8,16	1,2	2
6.	1,3,5,15 / 1,7	1	1
7.	1,2,3,4,6,8,12,24 / 1,2,3,6,9,18	1,2,3,6	6

Page 34

	a	b	c			a	b	c
1.	$\frac{4}{5}$	$\frac{1}{2}$	$\frac{2}{3}$		4.	$6\frac{2}{3}$	$\frac{5}{6}$	$3\frac{3}{4}$
2.	$2\frac{1}{2}$	$3\frac{2}{3}$	$5\frac{4}{5}$		5.	$3\frac{4}{5}$	$3\frac{7}{9}$	$\frac{1}{2}$
3.	$2\frac{2}{3}$	$5\frac{3}{4}$	$5\frac{5}{6}$					

Page 35

	a	b	c	d
1.	$\frac{3}{10}$	$\frac{8}{15}$	$\frac{4}{9}$	$\frac{5}{42}$
2.	$\frac{3}{5}$	$\frac{5}{9}$	$\frac{4}{7}$	$\frac{4}{15}$
3.	$\frac{1}{3}$	$\frac{2}{3}$	$\frac{1}{4}$	$\frac{1}{6}$
4.	$\frac{9}{20}$	$\frac{3}{8}$	$\frac{4}{15}$	$\frac{3}{4}$
5.	$\frac{10}{21}$	$\frac{21}{80}$	$\frac{1}{2}$	$\frac{27}{35}$

Page 36

1. $\frac{3}{8}$ 3. $\frac{2}{5}$ 5. $\frac{1}{4}$ 7. $\frac{1}{6}$
2. $\frac{8}{15}$ 4. $\frac{1}{2}$ 6. $\frac{1}{3}$

Page 37

	a	b	c	d
1.	$3\frac{1}{3}$	$4\frac{4}{5}$	$4\frac{1}{2}$	$5\frac{1}{4}$
2.	$7\frac{1}{2}$	$1\frac{1}{2}$	$4\frac{1}{2}$	8
3.	$7\frac{1}{2}$	$6\frac{2}{3}$	$6\frac{4}{5}$	$18\frac{2}{3}$

Page 38

1. 2   3. $10\frac{1}{2}$ 5. 3   7. 16; 8
2. 8   4. $9\frac{3}{8}$ 6. 5

Answers for SPECTRUM MATHEMATICS (Green Book, Second Edition)

Page 39

	a	b	c	d			a	b	c	d
1.	$6\frac{8}{15}$	$4\frac{1}{12}$	$4\frac{1}{6}$	$7\frac{1}{9}$	3.		$8\frac{3}{4}$	$6\frac{3}{8}$	$5\frac{1}{4}$	$12\frac{1}{2}$
2.	$5\frac{2}{5}$	$4\frac{1}{4}$	$6\frac{2}{5}$	$3\frac{1}{5}$	4.		$32\frac{15}{16}$	$6\frac{1}{2}$	$1\frac{9}{16}$	$20\frac{5}{6}$

Page 40

1. $3\frac{5}{9}$ 3. $31\frac{7}{8}$ 5. $15\frac{3}{4}$ 7. 26   9. $3\frac{3}{4}$
2. 6   4. $4\frac{1}{12}$ 6. $25\frac{1}{3}$ 8. $5\frac{1}{4}$

Page 43

	a	b	c	d	e
1.	$\frac{3}{5}$	$\frac{6}{7}$	$1\frac{1}{4}$	$1\frac{1}{2}$	$1\frac{3}{4}$
2.	$5\frac{1}{6}$	$7\frac{1}{2}$	$4\frac{3}{4}$	$3\frac{3}{4}$	$1\frac{2}{5}$
3.	$\frac{9}{10}$	$1\frac{1}{3}$	$3\frac{3}{4}$	$5\frac{3}{4}$	$1\frac{2}{3}$
4.	$\frac{2}{3}$	$\frac{5}{8}$	$4\frac{1}{3}$	$1\frac{1}{3}$	$5\frac{3}{8}$
5.	$1\frac{1}{4}$	$\frac{1}{3}$	$1\frac{1}{5}$		$\frac{6}{7}$

Page 44

1. $\frac{1}{2}$ 3. $\frac{3}{4}$ 5. $\frac{1}{6}$ 7. 1
2. $2\frac{1}{2}$ 4. $\frac{5}{8}$ 6. $1\frac{1}{2}$ 8. $\frac{2}{3}$

Page 45

	a	b	c	d			a	b	c	d
1.	$1\frac{4}{15}$	$1\frac{1}{30}$	$\frac{5}{6}$	$\frac{19}{30}$	3.		$1\frac{5}{24}$	$\frac{13}{24}$	$1\frac{3}{20}$	$\frac{1}{6}$
2.	$\frac{5}{12}$	$\frac{13}{30}$	$\frac{5}{24}$	$\frac{5}{12}$	4.		$1\frac{1}{12}$	$\frac{4}{15}$	$1\frac{3}{10}$	$\frac{1}{12}$

Page 46

	a	b	c	d
1.	$\frac{9}{10}$	$\frac{11}{15}$	$1\frac{1}{4}$	$1\frac{1}{8}$
2.	$\frac{5}{12}$	$\frac{1}{10}$	$1\frac{1}{2}$	$1\frac{1}{5}$
3.	$1\frac{2}{5}$	$\frac{1}{12}$	$1\frac{1}{3}$	$1\frac{1}{2}$
4.	$1\frac{1}{2}$	$\frac{2}{3}$	$1\frac{2}{15}$	$1\frac{2}{5}$

Page 47

	a	b	c	d
1.	$6\frac{1}{20}$	$3\frac{11}{12}$	$7\frac{1}{8}$	$4\frac{3}{4}$
2.	$10\frac{5}{8}$	$11\frac{7}{10}$	$3\frac{13}{30}$	$4\frac{11}{15}$
3.	$8\frac{7}{12}$	$5\frac{19}{20}$	$7\frac{3}{4}$	7
4.	$4\frac{23}{30}$	$6\frac{5}{24}$	$6\frac{5}{8}$	$8\frac{17}{30}$

Page 48

	a	b	c	d
1.	$6\frac{1}{4}$	$3\frac{1}{2}$	$4\frac{1}{3}$	$7\frac{7}{8}$
2.	$2\frac{3}{10}$	$2\frac{2}{9}$	$3\frac{1}{3}$	$2\frac{1}{2}$
3.	$4\frac{2}{5}$	$1\frac{5}{8}$	$1\frac{1}{6}$	$7\frac{7}{10}$
4.	$3\frac{5}{12}$	$7\frac{3}{8}$	$7\frac{1}{2}$	$5\frac{1}{10}$

Page 49

	a	b	c	d
1.	$\frac{3}{4}$	$\frac{11}{12}$	$3\frac{11}{12}$	$1\frac{9}{12}$
2.	$6\frac{1}{2}$	$1\frac{1}{2}$	$1\frac{5}{12}$	$1\frac{19}{24}$
3.	$3\frac{4}{5}$	$2\frac{1}{2}$	$6\frac{3}{4}$	$4\frac{4}{5}$
4.	$1\frac{19}{20}$	$5\frac{5}{8}$	$6\frac{5}{6}$	$6\frac{5}{12}$

Page 50

1. $\frac{5}{12}$ 3. $1\frac{1}{4}$ 5. $1\frac{1}{10}$ 7. $1\frac{7}{40}$
2. $\frac{9}{20}$ 4. $\frac{5}{8}$ 6. $\frac{1}{10}$ 8. $\frac{23}{40}$

Page 51

	a	b	c	d
1.	$1\frac{1}{2}$	$\frac{3}{8}$	1	$\frac{2}{3}$
2.	$1\frac{3}{8}$	$\frac{2}{15}$	$1\frac{5}{18}$	$\frac{1}{3}$
3.	$8\frac{4}{9}$	$\frac{7}{10}$	$5\frac{1}{8}$	$8\frac{1}{4}$
4.	$4\frac{7}{15}$	$6\frac{17}{24}$	$6\frac{7}{12}$	$\frac{7}{10}$
5.	$10\frac{5}{6}$	$14\frac{3}{4}$	$10\frac{29}{120}$	$8\frac{1}{3}$

Page 52

1. $2\frac{1}{8}$ 3. $4\frac{1}{4}$ 5. $5\frac{1}{8}$ 7. $\frac{19}{20}$
2. $\frac{3}{8}$ 4. $2\frac{1}{8}$ 6. $4\frac{33}{40}$

Page 55

	a	b	c	d	e	f
1.	$\frac{5}{3}$	$\frac{8}{7}$	$\frac{5}{4}$	$\frac{7}{5}$	$\frac{9}{4}$	$\frac{7}{6}$
2.	$\frac{3}{5}$	$\frac{7}{8}$	$\frac{4}{5}$	$\frac{5}{7}$	$\frac{4}{9}$	$\frac{6}{7}$
3.	8	3	4	9	16	14
4.	$\frac{1}{8}$	$\frac{1}{3}$	$\frac{1}{4}$	$\frac{1}{9}$	$\frac{1}{16}$	$\frac{1}{14}$
5.	$\frac{5}{8}$	$\frac{1}{3}$	$\frac{4}{3}$	$\frac{9}{6}$	$\frac{4}{16}$	$\frac{9}{8}$
6.	$\frac{5}{8}$	$\frac{9}{10}$	$\frac{3}{2}$	$\frac{6}{11}$	$\frac{7}{4}$	$\frac{9}{8}$
7.	$\frac{1}{15}$	$\frac{9}{10}$	$\frac{11}{12}$	$\frac{11}{17}$	$\frac{7}{9}$	$\frac{2}{17}$
8.	$\frac{8}{15}$	$\frac{5}{12}$	11	$\frac{7}{11}$	11	$\frac{5}{2}$
9.	$\frac{1}{10}$	$\frac{1}{13}$	17	$\frac{11}{12}$	$\frac{7}{9}$	$\frac{9}{2}$
10.	$\frac{8}{5}$	6	$\frac{1}{7}$	$\frac{7}{12}$		$9\frac{1}{2}$

Page 56

	a	b	c	d
1.	30	16	28	30
2.	49	$37\frac{1}{2}$	$42\frac{2}{3}$	$32\frac{2}{5}$
3.	54	16	34	16

Page 57

	a	b	c	d
1.	$\frac{1}{12}$	$\frac{1}{8}$	$\frac{1}{15}$	$\frac{1}{12}$
2.	$\frac{3}{20}$	$\frac{5}{16}$	$\frac{3}{16}$	$\frac{5}{18}$
3.	$\frac{1}{8}$	$\frac{1}{9}$	$\frac{1}{5}$	$\frac{1}{12}$

Page 58

1. $\frac{1}{6}$ 3. $\frac{1}{4}$ 5. $\frac{7}{32}$
2. $\frac{1}{8}$ 4. $\frac{1}{6}$ 6. $\frac{1}{6}$

Page 59

	a	b	c	d
1.	$\frac{2}{5}$	$\frac{2}{3}$	$\frac{1}{2}$	$\frac{2}{3}$
2.	$1\frac{1}{5}$	$\frac{6}{7}$	8	$1\frac{1}{4}$
3.	2	$\frac{1}{2}$	$2\frac{2}{9}$	$1\frac{1}{4}$

Page 60

1. 3   3. 6   5. 4   7. 5   9. 4
2. 3   4. $4\frac{1}{2}$ 6. 2   8. 2

Page 61

	a	b	c	d		a	b	c	d
1.	12	$\frac{4}{35}$	$\frac{1}{2}$	$\frac{9}{10}$	4.	$\frac{1}{5}$	2	$1\frac{1}{4}$	$7\frac{1}{2}$
2.	$1\frac{1}{4}$	24	$\frac{1}{6}$	$\frac{3}{7}$	5.	1	$\frac{27}{28}$	21	$\frac{3}{14}$
3.	$2\frac{1}{2}$	$1\frac{1}{8}$	15	$\frac{2}{27}$					

Page 62

1. 27　　3. 2　　5. $\frac{1}{8}$　　7. $\frac{1}{16}$
2. $\frac{1}{12}$　　4. 12　　6. $\frac{1}{2}$　　8. $\frac{3}{20}$

Page 63

	a	b	c	d
1.	$\frac{5}{6}$	$\frac{7}{15}$	3	$4\frac{1}{2}$
2.	$\frac{18}{35}$	$\frac{9}{20}$	$3\frac{3}{4}$	$1\frac{1}{2}$
3.	$6\frac{3}{10}$	$\frac{1}{9}$	$\frac{9}{25}$	$\frac{8}{15}$

Page 64

1. 4　　3. 3　　5. 9　　7. 6
2. 10　　4. 6　　6. 4

Page 67

	a	b	c	d
1.	.6	.2	.8	.5
2.	4.7	5.9	18.2	423.6
3.	$\frac{7}{10}$	$\frac{3}{10}$	$\frac{1}{10}$	$\frac{9}{10}$
4.	$4\frac{9}{10}$	$12\frac{7}{10}$	$15\frac{1}{10}$	$217\frac{3}{10}$
5.	.8	3.7		
6.	.4	25.8		
7.	.5	100.6		

8. nine tenths
9. three and seven tenths
10. twenty-one and two tenths

Page 68

	a	b	c
1.	.08	.16	.05
2.	1.36	8.06	9.12
3.	12.45	43.67	26.04
4.	142.08	436.42	389.89
5.	$\frac{17}{100}$	$\frac{3}{100}$	$\frac{41}{100}$
6.	$5\frac{19}{100}$	$6\frac{47}{100}$	$5\frac{1}{100}$
7.	$21\frac{7}{100}$	$23\frac{99}{100}$	$44\frac{89}{100}$
8.	$142\frac{33}{100}$	$483\frac{3}{100}$	$185\frac{63}{100}$

	a	b
9.	.08	6.23
10.	.95	14.60
11.	.48	4.44

Page 69

	a	b	c
1.	.008	.017	.0054
2.	.0125	.430	.0306
3.	4.004	3.0041	6.183
4.	35.0078	42.019	196.006
5.	$\frac{9}{1000}$	$\frac{19}{10000}$	$\frac{3}{10000}$
6.	$\frac{123}{1000}$	$\frac{441}{10000}$	$\frac{219}{1000}$
7.	$4\frac{11}{1000}$	$2\frac{1011}{10000}$	$6\frac{14}{10000}$
8.	$36\frac{37}{1000}$	$3\frac{433}{1000}$	$100\frac{1}{10000}$

	a	b
9.	.053	10.009
10.	.0011	12.018
11.	.065	12.001

Page 70

	a	b	c		a	b	c
1.	.6	.60	.600	3.	2.8	.35	.056
2.	3.5	.28	2.190	4.	2.2	.38	.352

Page 71

	a	b	c	d
1.	$\frac{3}{10}$	$\frac{1}{10}$	$\frac{2}{5}$	$\frac{1}{2}$
2.	$2\frac{7}{10}$	$3\frac{3}{10}$	$7\frac{1}{5}$	$5\frac{4}{5}$
3.	$\frac{17}{100}$	$\frac{3}{100}$	$\frac{3}{20}$	$\frac{4}{5}$
4.	$5\frac{7}{100}$	$8\frac{43}{100}$	$4\frac{1}{20}$	$2\frac{11}{25}$
5.	$\frac{3}{1000}$	$\frac{17}{1000}$	$\frac{1}{8}$	$\frac{9}{200}$
6.	$3\frac{121}{1000}$	$2\frac{987}{1000}$	$4\frac{1}{4}$	$3\frac{1}{125}$
7.	$4\frac{7}{100}$	$\frac{7}{10}$	$6\frac{1}{5}$	$1\frac{7}{1000}$
8.	$2\frac{3}{5}$	$3\frac{6}{25}$	$5\frac{1}{4}$	$3\frac{1}{2}$
9.	$5\frac{1}{8}$	$\frac{7}{10}$	$2\frac{2}{5}$	$\frac{1}{25}$
10.	$\frac{1}{100}$	$\frac{51}{1000}$	$\frac{4}{5}$	$2\frac{19}{100}$

Page 72

	a	b	c	d
1.	.2	.35	.445	
2.	7.5	4.58	3.360	
3.	$\frac{9}{10}$	$3\frac{3}{5}$	$\frac{7}{20}$	$17\frac{3}{4}$
4.	$\frac{1}{40}$	$8\frac{89}{200}$	$24\frac{61}{100}$	$8\frac{1}{20}$
5.	$\frac{3}{5}$	.6	.60	
6.	$2\frac{7}{10}$	2.7		2.700
7.	$5\frac{2}{5}$		5.40	5.400
8.		3.5	3.50	3.500
9.	$17\frac{9}{10}$		17.90	17.900
10.	$80\frac{4}{5}$	80.8		80.800

Page 73

	a	b	c	d	e
1.	.9	1.7	12.6	32.1	52.4
2.	.77	1.24	7.94	96.81	62.21
3.	.245	1.332	4.339	5.813	43.223
4.	1.8	7.5	9.9	46.8	8.4
5.	1.00	$1.04	10.54	$41.89	$37.19
6.	.721	.696	10.620	6.329	38.114

Page 74

1. 2　　3. 8　　5. .218　　7. 7.1
2. 1.5　　4. .63　　6. 3.9　　8. 16

Page 75

	a	b	c	d	e
1.	1.32	1.23	1.001	1.143	.845
2.	6.058	13.14	4.116	8.333	34.43
3.	1.238	.96	2.48	1.081	.915
4.	7.122	16.837	10.944	11.461	10.104

	a	b
5.	1.71	1.166
6.	.694	.853
7.	1.201	8.024
8.	2.71	26.556

Page 76

1. 1.25　　3. 1.225　　5. $66.55　　7. $43.50
2. 1.50 or 1.5　　4. 1.175　　6. $26.55　　8. 5.495

Page 77

	a	b	c	d	e
1.	.4	.7	.4	.8	.3
2.	.11	.33	.05	.48	$.15
3.	.111	.289	.208	.439	.379
4.	1.4	4.6	4.9	4.9	18.3
5.	3.13	$3.82	3.69	$12.65	$3.77
6.	2.212	2.209	2.812	23.802	11.196
7.	10.4	2.48	7.13	1.955	12.388

Page 78

1. .2	3. .23	5. 2.775	7. 1.8
2. .5	4. .24	6. 2.40	

Page 79

	a	b	c	d	e
1.	.52	2.16	2.68	3.216	.646
2.	.113	.293	4.861	2.748	.982
3.	.45	.24	5.18	4.65	7.58
4.	.591	.125	2.044	2.868	10.686
5.	.436	.085	4.408	3.788	10.536
6.	32.085	38.925	39.036	23.85	1.076
7.	37.52	318.79	1.026	78.667	89.397

Page 80

1. Ralph; 6.05	3. 8.006	5. 7.187
2. .35	4. .819	

Page 83

	a	b	c	d	e
1.	6	.6	.06	.006	.6
2.	48	4.8	.48	.048	.48
3.	15	1.5	.15	.015	.015
4.	12	.12	.012	.012	.0012
5.	42	.42	.042	.042	.0042
6.	72	.72	.072	.072	.0072

Page 84

	a	b	c	d
1.	44.8	4.48	.448	.0448
2.	129.6	12.96	1.296	.1296
3.	8.84	.884	.0884	88.4
4.	1.924	192.4	19.24	.1924
5.	7.5	.075	.75	.0075
6.	.48	.48	.048	.0048
7.	2.19	.0219	2.19	.219

Page 85

	a	b	c	d	e
1.	3.5	.6	7.2	2.1	.8
2.	.48	.06	.21	.08	.42
3.	.32	.06	.56	.54	.15
4.	.045	.035	.064	.006	.015
5.	.0024	.0024	.0009	.0056	.0006
6.	.063	.048	.024	.032	.035
7.	.0045	.0081	.0012	.0009	.0025

Page 86

	a	b	c	d	e
1.	56.42	564.2	5642	5642	5.642
2.	1.064	10.64	106.4	.106	1064
3.	2.3	23	230	.23	.23
4.	.08	.8	8	8	80
5.	15	150	1500	1500	1.5

Page 87

	a	b	c	d	e
1.	3.44	.216	.0532	.0162	.736
2.	.0411	38.56	362.8	4.571	2.496
3.	16.05	20.24	.2836	.0842	.4527
4.	1.134	.928	.075	.2226	57.76
5.	.6545	3.528	85.33	.4464	3.9075
6.	75.888	9.2796	73.536	.8164	.5328

Page 88

1. 5.4	4. 21.05	7. 3.7996
2. .168	5. .144	8. 478.8
3. 3	6. .192	9. 411.6

Page 89

	a	b	c	d
1.	.24	.72	.0049	.040
2.	1.215	.1216	.1118	18.75
3.	7.897	1.9992	16.324	4.4469
4.	9.5742	114.552	254.904	34.4258
5.	38.5014	175.417	19.4688	45.0294

Page 90

1. 40.8	4. 1110.06	7. 94.864
2. .336	5. .22435	8. 94864
3. 1.608	6. 3270	

Page 93

	a	b	c	d	e
1.	73	7.3	.73	.073	.0073
2.	1.87	.0027	.033	1.16	4.2
3.	3.5	.042	.0027	6.1	.56

Page 94

1. .2	3. .003	5. .001	7. .012
2. 2.3	4. .06	6. 18.1	8. .0084

Page 95

	a	b	c	d
1.	180	270	510	370
2.	1800	2400	1700	3700
3.	3000	3000	4000	31000

Page 96

1. 180	3. 13000	5. 240	7. 1000
2. 130	4. 650	6. 1250	8. 12

Page 97

	a	b	c	d
1.	18	2.7	.49	92
2.	14	1.7	2.8	36
3.	4	.6	18	3.7
4.	24	70	1.5	12

Page 98

	a	b	c	d
1.	60	480	230	30
2.	800	50	270	500
3.	370	1700	340	1200
4.	65	70	200	140
5.	250	8100	830	9600

Page 99

	a	b	c		a	b	c
1.	.48	2.9	.017	4.	140	1800	280
2.	150	4000	200	5.	120	28000	1.6
3.	1.4	5300	7.9				

Page 100

1. 18   3. 1700   5. 840   7. 100
2. 1; .5   4. .65   6. 10

Page 101

	a	b	c	d
1.	5	60	500	500
2.	3.3	1.8	4.6	.25
3.	.58	2.7	4.2	.032
4.	3000	4.2	.073	1.2

Page 102

1. 8   3. 80   5. 4   7. 100
2. 3; .7   4. 8   6. 5   8. .01

Page 103

	a	b	c		a	b	c
1.	8.2	.12	500	3.	.47	2.8	9.2
2.	3.3	120	76				

Page 104

1. 1.33   3. 40   5. .25   7. .01
2. 9.2   4. 9.5   6. .024

Page 107

1–3. Have your teacher check your work.
4. 7   6. 75
5. 5   7. 42

8–10. Have your teacher check your work.

Page 108

	a	b	c
1.	45	4.5	.045
2.	16	1.6	.016
3.	29	2.9	.029
4.	51	5.1	.051
5.	63	6.3	.063

	a	b	c
6.	5.4	8000	.234
7.	160	9	5.8
8.	.612	4000	1.3
9.	20	750	.0345
10.	7.07	.5	46.5

Page 109

	a	b
1.	4; 2; 8	1.5; 1.5; 2.25
2.	30; 15; 450	25; 10; 250
3.	17.4	
4.	20.25	
5.	518.4	

Page 110

1. 11250   4. 8400   7. 800000
2. 27   5. 1820
3. 55.25   6. 119

Page 111

	a	b	c
1.	54	64	162
2.	18.75	894.6	.18
3.	210		
4.	124.2		
5.	614.125		
6.	232.128		

Page 112

1–2. Have your teacher check your work.
3. 2.4
4. 588
5. 262.5

Page 113

1. 5000   3. 25   5. 96000
2. 24   4. 8

Page 114

	a	b
1.	7000	500
2.	.005	4.5
3.	7500	2540
4.	.6	.0075
5.	3400	.3
6.	3000	.3
7.	.0006	24000
8.	.047	750
9.	20000; 20	

Page 115

1. 50   3. 200   5. 210
2. 1000   4. 1000

Page 116

	a	b
1.	8000	7500
2.	4.5	.038
3.	6000	.64
4.	50	4500
5.	7	7
6.	5500	210
7.	400	.345
8.	.607	8900
9.	52000	.975
10.	50000	

Page 119

	a	b	
1.	72	5	7. 64
2.	27	4	8. 113
3.	180	4	9. 17
4.	15840	5280	10. 114
5.	15	$1\frac{1}{2}$	11. 6030
6.	10560	8800	

Page 120

1. 7   4. 51   7. 32
2. 112   5. 69   8. 59
3. 375   6. 46   9. 64

Answers for SPECTRUM MATHEMATICS (Green Book, Second Edition)

Page 121

	a	b	c		
1.	54	44	49	4. $17\frac{1}{2}$	6. $8\frac{3}{4}$
2.	$3\frac{3}{4}$	$24\frac{3}{4}$	$37\frac{1}{2}$	5. $13\frac{1}{2}$	7. $3\frac{3}{4}$
3.	36				

Page 122

1. 64	3. 231	5. 9600	7. $229\frac{1}{2}$
2. 140	4. 216	6. 100	

Page 123

	a	b	c		
1.	48	91	$65\frac{1}{4}$	6.	$115\frac{1}{2}$
2.	$82\frac{1}{2}$	$28\frac{1}{2}$	$56\frac{1}{4}$	7.	$35\frac{3}{4}$
3.	105			8.	$146\frac{1}{4}$
4.	$202\frac{1}{2}$			9.	$55\frac{1}{8}$
5.	$175\frac{1}{2}$			10.	$404\frac{11}{16}$

Page 124

1. 4200	3. 3072	5. 25200	7. 2592
2. 450	4. $37\frac{1}{2}$	6. $87\frac{3}{4}$	8. 48

Page 125

	a	b	
1.	6	4	5. 5
2.	10	5	6. 23
3.	16	$2\frac{3}{4}$	7. 5
4.	6	$7\frac{1}{2}$	8. 19
			9. 15; 30; 60

Page 126

	a	b	
1.	1152	5	7. 6500
2.	8000	3	8. 165
3.	180	2	9. 108
4.	300	6	10. 260
5.	120	6	11. 56
6.	60	86	

Page 129

1.	$\frac{1}{100}$	.01	8.	$\frac{49}{100}$	.49
2.	$\frac{7}{100}$	.07	9.	$\frac{61}{100}$	.61
3.	$\frac{29}{100}$	.29	10.	$\frac{9}{100}$	.09
4.	$\frac{47}{100}$	.47	11.	$\frac{37}{100}$	.37
5.	$\frac{53}{100}$	.53	12.	$\frac{77}{100}$	.77
6.	$\frac{21}{100}$	.21	13.	$\frac{91}{100}$	.91
7.	$\frac{83}{100}$	.83	14.	$\frac{33}{100}$	.33

Page 130

	a	b	c		a	b	c
1.	$\frac{1}{4}$	$\frac{9}{20}$	$1\frac{3}{5}$	6.	20%	75%	5%
2.	$\frac{13}{20}$	$1\frac{1}{5}$	$\frac{6}{25}$	7.	214%	60%	120%
3.	$\frac{39}{50}$	$\frac{11}{20}$	$2\frac{3}{5}$	8.	90%	28%	225%
4.	$\frac{7}{10}$	$1\frac{11}{25}$	$\frac{43}{50}$	9.	160%	30%	16%
5.	$\frac{19}{20}$	$2\frac{2}{5}$	$1\frac{4}{5}$	10.	35%	62%	140%

Page 131

	a	b	c
1.	.135	.37	.0625
2.	.065	.0475	.0275
3.	.07	.625	.085
4.	.325	.0875	.095
5.	.0825	.175	.0375
6.	.0075	.0725	.0175
7.	60%	52%	32.5%
8.	24.75%	80%	65%
9.	14.5%	16.75%	50%
10.	6%	.7%	6.25%
11.	7.5%	.75%	.5%
12.	90%	19%	38.5%

Page 132

1. 75%	3. .250	5. $\frac{9}{20}$	7. 98.7%
2. $\frac{13}{20}$	4. 80%	6. .615	8. 70%

Page 133

	a	b		a	b
1.	$4\frac{1}{2}$	$68\frac{29}{50}$	6.	$2\frac{71}{80}$	128
2.	16	$9\frac{9}{20}$	7.	$99\frac{3}{5}$	$1\frac{31}{50}$
3.	$13\frac{3}{5}$	$18\frac{1}{5}$	8.	$5\frac{11}{50}$	336
4.	$2\frac{2}{5}$	$7\frac{43}{50}$	9.	$5\frac{22}{25}$	225
5.	$36\frac{2}{5}$	$10\frac{1}{5}$	10.	725	$3\frac{21}{25}$

Page 134

1. 33	3. $140	5. $6	7. 3760
2. 150	4. 10	6. $4200	

Page 135

	a	b		a	b
1.	17.5	2.55	7.	86.4	9.56
2.	69.35	.528	8.	392	66.725
3.	74.1	1.472	9.	96.5	12.6
4.	.425	163.8	10.	12.395	4.836
5.	43.75	78.125	11.	642	33.6
6.	571.2	6.048	12.	697.2	826.8

Page 136

1. $48	3. $73.50	5. $1.23
2. $16.80	4. $3.90	

Page 139

	a	b	c	d	e
1.	98	385	2818	6187	52699
2.	83	786	5259	6328	70128
3.	.9	11.1	.88	90.23	9.949
4.	4.6	47.4	49.18	49.886	174.642

	a	b	c	d
5.	$\frac{5}{7}$	$\frac{7}{9}$	$\frac{3}{4}$	$1\frac{1}{2}$
6.	$\frac{7}{8}$	$\frac{13}{15}$	$1\frac{5}{12}$	$1\frac{3}{20}$
7.	$2\frac{19}{24}$	$2\frac{31}{35}$	$14\frac{5}{12}$	$12\frac{7}{12}$

Page 140

1. 574	3. $12\frac{1}{2}$	5. $67\frac{1}{8}$	7. $7\frac{2}{3}$
2. 39.23	4. 142.8	6. 93.9	

Page 141

	a	b	c	d	e
1.	54	211	4022	5653	51210
2.	55	511	1149	3462	23107
3.	49	608	2954	759	38943
4.	.5	.97	.57	6.471	1.109
5.	.9	4.81	8.29	6.288	62.986

	a	b	c	d
6.	$\frac{3}{7}$	$\frac{2}{9}$	$\frac{1}{3}$	$\frac{1}{2}$
7.	$\frac{1}{12}$	$\frac{1}{2}$	$\frac{7}{24}$	$\frac{13}{36}$
8.	$1\frac{3}{4}$	$3\frac{19}{24}$	$1\frac{7}{12}$	$2\frac{13}{20}$

Page 142

1. 2786   3. $43\frac{3}{4}$ 5. .025   7. 7.62
2. 1.8   4. 44449   6. $8\frac{3}{4}$

Page 143

	a	b	c	d	e
1.	224	648	4624	9639	60813
2.	576	10146	278553	206790	2811506
3.	71.4	79.36	17.898	6.4792	27.9091

	a	b	c	d
4.	$\frac{3}{8}$	$\frac{16}{35}$	$\frac{35}{16}$	$1\frac{1}{4}$
5.	$1\frac{1}{2}$	$4\frac{3}{8}$	$5\frac{11}{16}$	$4\frac{2}{3}$

Page 144

1. 9020   3. $7\frac{1}{2}$ 5. 56.85   7. 11.25
2. 381.36 4. 14400   6. $\frac{1}{2}$ 8. $\frac{5}{6}$

Page 145

	a	b	c	d	e
1.	19	36 r4	161 r1	621	1279
2.	15	69 r52	40 r14	167	859 r15
3.	315	900	3.4	2.8	41

	a	b	c	d
4.	$\frac{2}{3}$	$2\frac{2}{7}$	$\frac{2}{9}$	$2\frac{1}{16}$
5.	$\frac{5}{8}$	$\frac{7}{11}$	$2\frac{19}{24}$	$2\frac{1}{4}$

Page 146

1. 46   3. 3466; 5   5. 5.4   7. $1\frac{11}{16}$
2. 749   4. 1.29   6. 12

Page 147

	a	b
1.	9000	.78
2.	430	.068
3.	16000	.419
4.	7000	6.500
5.	2000	.918
6.	8400	1.350
7.	.004	.3
8.	60	45
9.	6	11
10.	12	7
11.	$2\frac{1}{4}$	19
12.	80	124
13.	360	315
14.	96	80

	a	b	c
15.	375	68	75

Page 148

1.	.25	25%	10. 24
2.	.5 or .50	50%	11. 174
3.	.6 or .60	60%	12. 121
4.	$\frac{2}{5}$	40%	13. 22.75
5.	$\frac{3}{100}$	3%	14. 42
6.	$\frac{5}{8}$	62.5%	15. 105
7.	$\frac{7}{100}$	.07	16. 48
8.	$\frac{3}{8}$	.375	
9.	$\frac{19}{20}$	.95	

Page 149

1. 81   3. 450   5. 68   7. 3.90
2. 312   4. 312   6. 3927   8. 150

Page 2

	a	b	c	d	e	f
1.	38	50	68	95	125	122
2.	41	48	15	85	89	179
3.	769	761	975	1390	601	1520
4.	613	433	592	527	1575	2899
5.	7788	10010	10263	17190	11011	
6.	3131	1779	44298	28693	36897	
7.	85758	59473	84125	55133	81222	
8.	51123	23008	39019	55705	69676	
9.	106	1697	9542	72937	84173	

Page 11

	a	b	c	d	e
1.	51	158	154	276	631
2.	48	12	79	169	97
3.	399	7089	3686	7845	30385
4.	14313	12812	85374	53966	80097

5. subtract; 3926   6. add; 62842   7. 95066

Page 12

	a	b	c	d	e
1.	99	192	608	3456	2468
2.	33945	2793	15504	27082	260235
3.	39483	250560	171864	2181114	4192533
4.	9	37	17 r4	325	38
5.	147 r1	135	785	2444 r8	724 r62

Page 25

	a	b	c	d	e
1.	86	342	4056	8106	50778
2.	805	3648	5115	86352	137566
3.	43776	54825	426512	1366530	1126428
4.	4	35	14 r39	116 r24	58 r20
5.	135	27 r15	1016 r32	3844 r5	434

Page 26

	a	b	c	d
1.	$\frac{3}{10}$	$\frac{16}{35}$	$\frac{10}{21}$	$\frac{4}{25}$
2.	$\frac{1}{10}$	$\frac{5}{24}$	$\frac{9}{28}$	$\frac{4}{15}$
3.	$1\frac{1}{5}$	$4\frac{4}{9}$	$4\frac{1}{2}$	$2\frac{2}{3}$
4.	$13\frac{1}{3}$	$12\frac{1}{2}$	$2\frac{2}{3}$	$10\frac{1}{2}$
5.	$2\frac{11}{12}$	$2\frac{23}{56}$	$6\frac{2}{3}$	8

Page 41

	a	b	c	d		a	b	c	d
1.	$\frac{5}{12}$	$\frac{35}{48}$	$\frac{10}{21}$	$\frac{9}{64}$	4.	$13\frac{1}{3}$	$1\frac{3}{5}$	8	$3\frac{3}{4}$
2.	$\frac{10}{21}$	$\frac{28}{45}$	$\frac{3}{4}$	$\frac{1}{2}$	5.	$3\frac{17}{21}$	$6\frac{3}{10}$	$2\frac{14}{15}$	$11\frac{2}{3}$
3.	$1\frac{1}{5}$	$4\frac{2}{7}$	4	$6\frac{2}{3}$					

Page 42

	a	b	c	d		a	b	c	d
1.	$\frac{4}{7}$	$\frac{2}{3}$	$\frac{5}{8}$	$\frac{3}{5}$	4.	$3\frac{1}{4}$	$4\frac{23}{40}$	$5\frac{1}{9}$	$1\frac{3}{4}$
2.	$1\frac{1}{6}$	$1\frac{1}{4}$	$\frac{11}{24}$	$5\frac{11}{40}$	5.	$2\frac{5}{18}$	$4\frac{1}{2}$	$10\frac{7}{30}$	9
3.	$2\frac{3}{5}$	$\frac{1}{8}$	$5\frac{13}{30}$	$3\frac{9}{10}$					

Page 53

	a	b	c	d		a	b	c	d
1.	$\frac{7}{8}$	$\frac{1}{2}$	$1\frac{1}{6}$	$2\frac{9}{11}$	4.	$5\frac{13}{30}$	$3\frac{11}{40}$	$5\frac{13}{24}$	$6\frac{2}{3}$
2.	$1\frac{1}{18}$	$1\frac{5}{24}$	$1\frac{1}{2}$	$1\frac{1}{12}$	5.	$3\frac{17}{20}$	$3\frac{1}{8}$	$12\frac{59}{120}$	$11\frac{7}{24}$
3.	$5\frac{8}{9}$	$2\frac{3}{7}$	$5\frac{5}{24}$	$3\frac{5}{8}$					

Page 54

	a	b	d	c
1.	8	$10\frac{1}{2}$	10	$10\frac{1}{2}$
2.	$\frac{1}{8}$	$\frac{3}{10}$	$\frac{1}{7}$	$\frac{4}{27}$
3.	$\frac{2}{7}$	$1\frac{1}{2}$	2	$1\frac{1}{6}$
4.	$1\frac{1}{4}$	$\frac{9}{10}$	2	$1\frac{1}{3}$
5.	$\frac{3}{4}$	$2\frac{1}{2}$	$\frac{3}{14}$	$2\frac{1}{7}$

Page 65

	a	b	c	d		a	b	c	d
1.	15	$10\frac{2}{3}$	6	$11\frac{2}{3}$	4.	$1\frac{1}{2}$	$1\frac{1}{15}$	$1\frac{1}{6}$	$\frac{3}{4}$
2.	$\frac{1}{6}$	$\frac{4}{21}$	$\frac{1}{9}$	$\frac{3}{28}$	5.	$\frac{7}{15}$	$3\frac{3}{5}$	$\frac{6}{9}$	$2\frac{2}{9}$
3.	$\frac{4}{9}$	$\frac{1}{2}$	2	$1\frac{1}{3}$					

Page 66

	a	b	c
1.	.7	3.19	5.025
2.	.8	3.32	3.128
3.	$\frac{4}{5}$	$9\frac{33}{100}$	$16\frac{1}{8}$

	a	b	c	d
4.	.8	1.07	8.023	14.076
5.	1.1	.76	.438	10.274
6.	1.08	1.086	7.525	46.208
7.	.32	3.317	3.55	.285

Page 81

	a	b	c
1.	.175	9.4	3.08
2.	.90	3.2	5.300
3.	$\frac{3}{40}$	$8\frac{3}{5}$	$16\frac{49}{100}$

	a	b	c	d
4.	1.3	.95	14.361	30.646
5.	1.7	4.51	.067	5.697
6.	1.32	.415	18.273	57.355
7.	.166	2.59	2.784	4.825

Page 82

	a	b	c	d	e
1.	3.5	.8	3.6	1.2	3
2.	.42	.06	.32	.72	.4
3.	.012	.008	.006	.004	.012
4.	.21	.08	.24	.54	.4
5.	.048	.005	.006	.0042	.0004
6.	4	.8	67.2	234	5680
7.	4.8	.235	.272	1.2525	.585

Page 91

	a	b	c	d	e
1.	.48	1.26	.2772	2.226	4.844
2.	5.4	.72	29.82	.48	75.92
3.	.015	.576	2.835	35.38	14.952
4.	.08	.212	.2408	118.712	162.8
5.	.0054	.0134	37.24	15.5944	264.176

Page 92

	a	b	c	d
1.	7.3	.27	.045	.0019
2.	20	150	2100	4000
3.	1.2	21	2.4	5
4.	80	60	3630	600
5.	150	.14	.46	.92

Page 105

	a	b	c	d
1.	.023	.14	3.7	.0051
2.	1100	12000	60	2100
3.	23	1.4	2.4	7
4.	900	70	90	10300
5.	25	1.4	2.6	.073

Page 106

	a	b		a	b
1.	7000	.085	5.	3500	.0065
2.	190	.045	6.	8200	.255
3.	6000	.007	7.	289	8.5
4.	5000	4	8.	90	45

Page 117

	a	b		a	b
1.	9000	.365	6.	900	.785
2.	720	.084	7.	2000	998
3.	26000	.017	8.	1.5	450
4.	4510	.065	9.	25.2	9.8
5.	6800	3.5	10.	240	70.2

Page 118

	a	b	
1.	36	4	9. 56
2.	18	8	10. 15
3.	10560	5280	11. 38
4.	6	7	12. 150
5.	14	2	
6.	32	1	
7.	360	3	
8.	2	2	

	a	b
13.	28	18
14.	330	

Page 127

	a	b		a	b
1.	96	6	9.	70	48
2.	15	10	10.	17	3
3.	10560	1760	11. 76		
4.	12	$5\frac{1}{2}$	12. 210		
5.	36	6	13. 4320		
6.	20	2			
7.	96	2			
8.	300	2			

	a	b
14.	56	45

Page 128

	a	b
1.	7	90
2.	35	52
3.	7	40
4.	13.5	135
5.	.06	.67
6.	.0625	1.25
7.	$\frac{9}{100}$	$\frac{1}{5}$
8.	$\frac{9}{20}$	$\frac{14}{25}$
9.	.59 or $\frac{59}{100}$	7.5 or $7\frac{1}{2}$
10.	84	40.05 or $40\frac{1}{20}$
11.	36	122.01 or $122\frac{1}{100}$
12.	21.6 or $21\frac{3}{5}$	63
13.	33.75	8.194
14.	52.5	5.551

Page 137

1.	.03	3%	11. 16
2.	.25	25%	12. 62.4 or $62\frac{2}{5}$
3.	.35	35%	13. 43.75
4.	$\frac{3}{50}$	6%	14. 20.28
5.	$\frac{39}{100}$	39%	15. 8.228
6.	$\frac{1}{8}$	12.5%	
7.	$\frac{1}{20}$	.05	
8.	$\frac{7}{25}$	.28	
9.	$\frac{3}{4}$	.75	
10.	$\frac{9}{10}$	.9	

Page 138

	a	b	c	d	e
1.	2595	86.18	22.898	$11\frac{3}{4}$	$9\frac{13}{24}$
2.	5351	72.635	152.853	$7\frac{5}{8}$	$2\frac{14}{15}$
3.	260145	13.5063	127 r36	25.3	
4.	$\frac{10}{21}$	$4\frac{7}{12}$	$1\frac{2}{7}$	$\frac{35}{64}$	
5.	6000	$7\frac{1}{2}$ or 7.5			
6.	249	19.5			
7.	20	$62\frac{1}{2}$ or 62.5			

Page 150

	a	b	c	d
1.	62.676	$1\frac{19}{24}$	1014.913	$13\frac{7}{8}$
2.	254375	31 r12	10.4636	4.5
3.	$\frac{15}{32}$	$1\frac{5}{16}$	$6\frac{1}{6}$	$7\frac{7}{9}$

	a	b
4.	5000	24
5.	6	23.925

6. 117	8. 30
7. $35\frac{3}{4}$	9. $28\frac{1}{8}$

9 10 11 12 13 14 15   876